BEETROOT

The Vitality Plant
& Its Medicinal Benefits

BEETROOT

The Vitality Plant
& Its Medicinal Benefits

Margaret Briggs

Abbeydale Press

ISBN 978-1-86147-230-4

1 3 5 7 9 10 8 6 4 2

Published by Abbeydale Press
an imprint of Bookmart Ltd
Registered number 2372865
Trading as Bookmart Ltd
Blaby Road, Wigston, Leicester
LE18 4SE, England

Produced for Bookmart Limited
Illustrations by Tegan Sharrard
Cover design by Omnipress Ltd

Printed in Dubai

ABOUT THE AUTHOR

Margaret Briggs was a teacher for 30 years, working in Kent,
Germany, North Yorkshire and Sussex.

Since leaving teaching she has had more time for gardening and
cooking and has embarked on a second career as a freelance
writer, researcher and editor, alongside her writer husband, Lol.
Six years ago the couple bought a dilapidated house in south-
west France. The house is now restored and Margaret and Lol
divide their time between Sussex and the Gironde, with two
contrasting gardens to develop.

Margaret has written four other books in this series, *Vinegar —
1001 Practical Uses*, *Gardening Hints and Tips*, *Porridge — Oats
and their Many Uses* and *Honey — and its many health benefits*.

CONTENTS

Introduction 7

Know your beetroot 9

The history behind beetroot 15

The sugar trail 27

Commercial uses of beetroot 33

The nutritional value of beetroot and
chard 47

Health benefits throughout history 57

Growing your own beetroot 71

Growing perpetual spinach and chard 89

Cooking with beetroot 95

Spinach recipes 137

Alphabetical list of spinach beets
and chards 158

Introduction

The group of plants belonging to the family *Beta vulgaris* are classy vegetables. There's nothing vulgar about them and so much more than initially meets the eye. From their humble beginnings as wild sea beet man has produced a number of invaluable crops for humans and animals. Who would imagine that so many benefits to health and such a variety of tastes would result? Millions of animals are fed, thanks to the modern mangelwurzel and the whole of the sugar beet industry has developed from it. Economies around the world rely on sugar production and beets might even provide a partial answer to biofuels of the future. At the other end of the plant breeding world, *Beta vulgaris* provides two forms of vegetables packed full of the vitamins and minerals so often missing from today's processed foods.

Our ancestors harnessed the beneficial qualities of beetroot to cure or treat a whole range of ailments, and modern scientific research has confirmed what they already knew, or suspected, from just eating beetroot and spinach beet. Today, beetroot is acknowledged as a valuable resource in the prevention of heart disease and cancer and a whole host of treatments for other problems, including depression.

This book will take you through some of the history around beetroot and help to explain how beetroot and spinach can provide so many of the nutrients we need in our modern lives. If you don't know your Rouge Crapaudine from Bluto or your Crosby's Egyptian from your Pablo, read on.

If, like me, you were put off beetroot as a child, this may be the time to look at the recipes and give it another go. You never know, eating it once or twice a week may change your life!

Know Your Beetroot

The latin name for beetroot is *Beta vulgaris*. It is a flowering member of the *Chenopodiaceae* — or goosefoot — family of plants which are native to western and southern Europe and also includes other edible species, including spinach. Its importance in food terms is widespread, because its cultivated varieties produce not only beetroot for the table, but also fodder beets, leaf beets, such as chard and perpetual spinach, and the most important economically, sugar beet.

Beta vulgaris is classified as a herbaceous perennial or biennial plant. Its leafy stems grow up to two metres. The wild plants look similar to dock leaves, but the two plants are not related. The leaves are heart shaped and about 5 to 20 cm (2 to 8 in) long, although cultivated varieties can have much larger leaves. Tiny green or reddish flowers with five petals are produced on spikes. The seeds are produced as hard clusters, which are pollinated by the wind.

There are four sections within the Beta family, covering 10 species and three sub species. Those which concern this book are
- *Beta vulgaris maritima*, or wild sea beet
- *Beta vulgaris vulgaris*, which includes leaf beet, fodder beet and sugar beet

You can read about how the wild forms became used throughout history and the development of the various types in the History section.

BETA VULGARIS MARITIMA

Also known as Sea beet, this is the subspecies which all cultivated beets have come from. It is really a biennial, taking two years to reach maturity. In the first year the root is well developed, but it is not until the second year in most cases that the flowers and seeds develop and the plant can reproduce.

The *maritima* has long leaves arranged in a sort of rosette and it does not have a swollen root. In the wild, sea beets thrive on sandy or stony beaches, rocky cliffs, salt marshes and grasslands in coastal areas. The sea beet is also found in Iran, Azerbaijan and India.

BETA VULGARIS VULGARIS

These cultivated varieties can be broken down again.

- *Beta vulgaris cicla* — better known as leaf beets or chard.
- *Beta vulgaris conditiva* — known as beetroot or table beet.
- *Beta vulgaris alba* — or fodder beet.
- *Beta vulgaris altissima* — known as sugar beet.

BETA VULGARIS CICLA

There are two main types of leaf beets: Spinach beet or perpetual spinach and chard.

SPINACH BEET OR PERPETUAL SPINACH

This beet is grown for its leaves. It is different from true spinach, or *Spinacia oleracea* and New Zealand spinach. It does not have a thick leaf stem or a swollen taproot. Perpetual spinach has been eaten in Europe since ancient times. In parts of Ireland it is known as wild spinach. In India it is an important crop and is used widely in the cooking of vegetable dishes. It is also used extensively in parts of Central and South America.

CHARD

This is also known as Swiss chard, silver beet and seakale beet. Chard is grown for its foliage, which occurs in a variety of colourful forms. Cultivated varieties such as Lucullus, with its green leaf blades and white stem (one of the oldest varieties), Bright Yellow, Rhubarb, Rainbow or Ruby chard are prized for their appearance as well as taste. Chards have no swollen taproot, but a thickened stem. The leaves are shiny and ribbed and have a slightly bitter taste. Both the leaves and the stem are edible, but the stem can be tough.

Swiss chard has nothing to do with Switzerland and is not a native plant of that country. The name apparently comes from a botanist called Koch, who gave it the name in the 19th century.

Chard is also sometimes used to refer to the succulent stalk portions of leaves of globe artichokes and cardoon, a sort of Mediterranean celery. It has many things to recommend it, in terms of health, which you can read about in the Health and Nutrition section.

BETA VULGARIS CONDITIVA

Beetroot is most commonly known as a root vegetable, although the leaves are also edible. Larger varieties are grown as a winter root crop whereas smaller rooted varieties have become popular as summer salad crops. Most Mediterranean varieties are treated as annuals, however, and seed production is discouraged, otherwise the plant will have 'bolted'. You can read more about this later on.

Table beets have been selected to have less hard fibrous tissue than fodder and sugar beet varieties. The colour of the root depends on the presence of pigments called betalains. The purple pigment present in red beetroot is due to betacyanin and betaxanthin, which together are known as betanins. This is not the same pigment as is found in red cabbage, which is called anthocyanin. Not all beetroots are red/purple, however, and those which are white or golden do not contain as much betanin. You can read about different varieties in a later section. Betalains are used extensively in the food industry as a colourant and you can find out more about them in the section on Commercial Uses of Beetroot.

The pigment in beetroot is not stable unless it is in acidic conditions, which accounts for the 'bleeding' which occurs when beetroot is cut, heated or left in contact with sunlight and creates staining of surfaces it comes in contact with. For this reason, beetroot is usually cooked before removing the skin. This probably accounts for the fact that beetroot has frequently been treated by pickling it.

Table beets contain high amounts of vitamin C in the roots and vitamin A in the leaves. They also contain folate, antioxidants and dietary fibre. Beetroot is a sweet root vegetable and contains more sugar than carrots or maize (sweetcorn). Modern beetroot cultivars contain between 6% and 10% sucrose.

BETA VULGARIS ALBA

Both the roots and leaves are fed to animals and they are used as fresh food and silage. Fodder beets are often grouped again by the shape of the root into the following four categories:

- Globe or spherical
- Long
- Cylindrical
- Flat

One of the distinguishing features of fodder beets is that the swollen taproot may sit at least half way out of the ground. The colour of fodder beet ranges from scarlet, orange, pink and yellow to white, but the majority are white. The root is distinguished by its size and rougher texture. One of the reasons for the unpopularity of beetroot as a vegetable has been attributed to the fact that people associate it with animal food. One of the oldest varieties is called Mangel. It originated as a cross between leaf beet and beetroot.

Modern fodder varieties are a cross between mangel and sugar beet. The mangelwurzel was originally called mangoldwurzel, meaning 'root of the beet', but German speakers corrupted the term to mangelwurzel, meaning 'root of scarcity', and this name stuck as the name for fodder beets. Modern fodder beets contain about 3—5% sugar and about 6—8% protein.

BETA VULGARIS ALTISSIMA

Sugar beet is the most recently developed of the beets and the most important commercially. The cone shaped roots, which are whitish in colour, can be up to 50 cm (20 in) in length. Modern breeding has produced a root which is high in sugar content and has few variations. The girth of the root increases as the plant grows and if you cut a root across the centre you may see that there are round about 12 to 15 rings visible inside the root by the time the plant is ready for harvesting. The sugar content of modern sugar beets is around 18—20%. The highest concentration of sugar is to be found nearest the centre of the root. You can read about sugar beet production in the chapter beginning on page 27.

The History Behind Beetroot

FROM WILD BEGINNINGS

The original plant from which modern varieties of beetroot have been cultivated was a wild sea beet which is found growing in North Africa, the Middle East, parts of Asia and the coastal areas of Europe. Originally the plant was prized for its stems and leaves and it has probably been eaten since prehistoric times. Beet remains have been excavated from the pyramid at Saqqara, built around 2600 BC, and four charred beetroots, probably of the wild sea beet variety, were found in a Neolithic site in the Netherlands. One of the first reported cultivations of this wild sea beet, called Silga, was in the Hanging Gardens of Babylon, about 800 BC. The Ancient Greeks liked to eat colourful leaves of the chard variety and both the Greeks and the Romans used the leaves of beet as a herb.

GREEK BEET
Apollo, the Greek god of the sun, was offered beet at the temple in Delphi. It was used and written about around 420 BC by Aristophanes, who referred to it by the name 'Teutlon'. The philosopher Aristotle also described red beetroot, which would have been very unusual back then. Other writers described it as all manner of colours, from white, light and dark green and black. The Greeks used the leaves for medicinal purposes rather than for everyday consumption. Roman and Arab writers later described different coloured beets, including yellow and pink varieties.

WHAT DID THE ROMANS DO FOR BEETROOT?
Beetroot was mentioned by many Roman writers including Cato, Cicero and Pliny the Elder. In Roman times the white and black varieties of beetroot seemed to have been more plentiful and it was the Romans who first started to use the root — which they called Beta — more than the leaves, for both food and medicine. Selection of seeds from the varieties with the best swollen roots found growing naturally probably started the first cultivation of beetroot. Although the Romans still mainly considered it a medicinal plant — they also used it to make broth as a treatment for fevers and as a laxative

— gradually its use became more widespread as the vegetable gained popularity.

The broth mentioned above was produced by cooking the roots in a mix of honey and wine with salt and oil added. It was also boiled in water and it is probable that the discarded roots were eaten rather than wasting them, presumably by someone of the 'Waste not, want not' school of cookery. One report suggested adding a little chicken to the broth helped the flavour, which reminds me of the old story called Stone Soup. All you need is a stone and some water, but the soup is even better with a pinch of salt, some carrots, beef, turnip etc. Still, that's how recipes evolved and that's probably how the first early beetroot salad developed: all you needed was a cooked root or two, some mustard, oil and vinegar. This was how Pliny the Elder (AD 23—79) described the dish. Beetroot still hadn't made the big time as a common food, however.

ROMAN STITCH UP
The leaves and roots were included as ingredients in soups thickened with barley, stews of roots, leeks and meat and for stuffing pigs for roasting. This last party dish required chickens, songbirds, snails, sausages, dates, bulbs of some flowers, herbs, peppers, eggs and pine kernels along with the beetroot. The whole beast was then stitched up, covered with honey, wine, oil, herbs and spiced, then roasted. After that lot you can see why many Romans considered beet leaves a little short on flavour. Some Roman physicians suggested boiling the beets twice to rid them of the after effects of flatulence and stomach ache and thought that they were only suitable for consumption dressed with pepper, wine and other herbs. Perhaps they were just getting over the effects of a stuffed suckling pig.

THE EMPIRE AND BEYOND
The Romans also deserve recognition for having spread the distribution of white and black beets to other parts of the Roman Empire, especially northern Europe, where a cooler climate meant better growing conditions. The Emperor Charlemagne had beets growing in his gardens

and even passed an edict which specified beetroot as a plant which was to be grown in all the imperial grounds. This meant that beetroot spread across Gaul (France), Italy, Spain and Germany. Beetroot was introduced to Eastern Europe and the Middle East on trade routes to East Asia. By AD 850 beetroot had arrived in China, where it was grown for its leaves.

THE MIDDLE AGES

From Roman times to the 16th century leaf beet was grown and consumed as a herb. Throughout the Middle Ages beetroot was grown for its roots and was often called Roman beet. Grown as a beneficial herb, it was a popular addition to monastery gardens and physic gardens in France, Spain and Italy. Hildegard of Bingen, an 11th century abbess and healer, had a good understanding of herbs. During her incredibly full life, for which she eventually became canonised, she wrote about preparing the roots, which needed to be cooled to be more beneficial. However, the technique didn't really catch on, although beets continued to grow in popularity during this time in the former Roman Empire and throughout the Arab world. In Portugal the Arabic name for beetroot, acelga, was adopted and leaf beet, especially chard, is still called acelga today in Portugal and Spain.

SHAPE OF THINGS TO COME

The shape of beetroot in the Middle Ages was still carrot or long turnip shaped; not the big round, fat roots we know of today. I can't help but think of the fictional character Baldric, who had an obsession with turnips in the 'Blackadder' series. He would have been bitterly disappointed by their appearance, I should think.

ON RIGHT PLEASURE AND GOOD HEALTH

Not much is recorded about beetroot until the 14th century when the word 'bete' appeared in manuscripts. Then, in the 15th century, an Italian physician and cook wrote the first real recipe book to set the scene for modern Italian cooking and what has become commonly known as the 'Mediterranean diet'. The book, *De Honesta Voluptate*, (*On Right Pleasure and Good Health*) by Bartholomaeus Platina was a best seller among upper classes and scholars. He was heavily influenced by Arabic food and classicists from ancient times. He included recipes for what 15th century men and women should eat to remain healthy and prevent illness, suggesting that the way forward was to "eat well, perhaps frugally".

GARLIC BREATH

Some of the recipes weren't exactly frugal, but discussed the quality of a large variety of meat, fish, fruit and vegetables. It was the first book to outline how these foods ought to be prepared and served, in order to maintain a healthy diet. One suggestion was for a green sauce made from leaf beet (spinach) or chard, parsley and wheat. He also described how beetroot, roasted on a fire, sweetened the breath when eaten with garlic. I think a few million people might disagree with the garlic breath claim today. The mind boggles as to what the breath was like in the first place! Other claims to fame from the pages of Platina's tome include a recipe for bear, where the head was considered good to eat, and the suggestion that plague victims take cannabis as a cure. Very few copies of the original 93 page book have survived, but I bet some of Platina's ideas are not a million miles away from modern discussions on food and diet.

By the end of the 15th century *Beta vulgaris* was found everywhere in Europe and by this time it was being eaten as a root vegetable rather than for medicinal purposes. New varieties were developed, including one in Germany which had a distinctive red root which was quite different from the white and black varieties developed in Italy. A new and improved *Beta Romana* became the forerunner of modern cultivars of both the long turnip, shaped root and the stout, spherical varieties.

Roman beet was first recorded in Germany, not Italy, in 1558 and by 1576 this variety had also reached England. After this, Germany became the centre for further development, as gardeners found the soil and climate ideal for growing beetroot as a popular food. This popularity spread to Poland, Russia, Lithuania and the Ukraine and then to parts of Scandinavia. In central and eastern Europe it continued to make up part of the staple diet. Bortsch originated from this time. You can find some recipes for this soup later in the book. Beetroot was an ideal crop for lifting during the autumn and then eating during the long, cold, winter months.

In France at the beginning of the 17th century an author and scientist interested in the soil, called Olivier de Serres, wrote a text book for French agriculture entitled Théâtre d'Agriculture. Amongst other things, he recommended that wine growers plant several varieties of grapevines in their vineyards to balance the risk of crop failure and introduced the idea of crop rotation. He described a kind of 'parsnip which has recently arrived from Italy'. It had a red, rather fat root, with thick leaves which could also be eaten. He noted that the juice extracted from the root was like sugar syrup. It was to be quite some time yet, however, before the idea of extracting sugar from beets caught on.

Beet roots have been fed to cattle in France since the 16th century, along with parsnips, Jerusalem Artichokes and several other root vegetables commonly served at the table in many other countries. I remember, about 30 years ago, describing to a French friend the parsnips I had roasted for Sunday dinner. He was unfamiliar with the vegetable's taste, as his grandparents only grew them to feed to the cows. Similarly, the only artichokes familiar to him were the globe variety, eaten with a vinaigrette, unless he visited his grandmother, down on the farm.

Happily, beetroot is no longer confined to animal fodder, and our local French market in the south west of France sells several varieties based on the Rouge Crapaudine, which was first developed in France. The roots have very dark purple — almost black — skin which looks distinctly unappetising on account of the rough, pock marked and often spongy exterior. They are often sold ready cooked, sometimes covered in cinders from the fire.

Another black, elongated root which looks similar is the black radish, so care must be taken, or you'll get quite a surprise when you cut it.

Meanwhile, back in England, Roman beet was going down well. Up until Elizabethan times, only white beet was grown here. John Gerard, who started to study medicine and travelled widely as a ship's surgeon before turning botanist and gardener, was greatly in favour with Queen Elizabeth I. He described white beet with its thick, hard roots, in less than glowing terms; beetroot, for him, was not flavour of the month. In Gerard's Herball, he wrote of white beet, whose leaves were the edible part, as follows:

BETA ALBA

*...the white Beete is a cold and moist pot-herbe...
Being eaten when it is boyled, it quickly descendeth...
especially being taken with the broth
wherein it is sodden.*

By this he presumably meant that it wilted. He didn't give it great marks for presentation or flavour either, saying it '*nourisheth little or nothing*'. He got that one wrong, as you can find out later.

In the late 1500s Gerard was given a new variety of red beet from abroad, which he grew in his garden. He described this vegetable in the following passage as one:

*". . . which hath leaves very great, and red of colour,
as is all the rest of the plant, as well as root,
as stalke, and floures full of a perfect purple juyce
tending to redness: the middle rib of which leaves
are for the most part very broad and thicke, like the
middle part of the cabbage leafe, which is equall in
goodness with the leaves of the cabbage being boyled".*

He obviously recognized the possibilities this root vegetable might provide throughout the year, suggesting that the leaves

*"may be used in winter for a sallad herbe,
with vinegre, oyle and salt, and is not only pleasant
to the taste, but also delightful to the eye".*

Of Roman Beet, Gerard made some serving suggestions:

> *"The greater red Beet or Roman Beet, boyled and
> eaten with oyle, vinegre and pepper, is a most
> excellent and delicat sallad: but what might be made
> of the red and beautifull root (which is preferred
> before the leaves, as well as beautie as in goodness)
> I refer unto the curious and cunning cooke, who no
> doubt when hee had the view thereof, and is assured
> that it is both good and wholesome, will make thereof
> many and divers dishes, both faire and good".*

So, the famous chefs were mostly men back then, too.

Although leaves of beets are commonly used as spinach,
the annual variety, Spinacia, probably of Persian origin
and cultivated for its succulent leaves, was introduced
into Europe during the fifteenth century. Of spinach,
Gerard wrote

> *"It is eaten boiled, but yeeldeth little or no
> nourishment at all: it is something windie, and easily
> causeth a desire to vomit: it is used in sallades when
> it is young and tender. This herbe of all other
> pot-herbes and sallade herbes maketh the greatest
> diversitie of meates and sallades."*

Well, at least he was more enthused by the new
beetroot.

John Parkinson, a contemporary of Gerard seemed to
have been more enthusiastic still. He suggested that
gardens no longer needed to be kept just for producing
food and herbs for medicinal purposes, but also wrote
about the aesthetic pleasures plants could bring. His
book, entitled *A Garden of Pleasant Flowers: Paradisi in
Sole Paradisus Terrestris* (1629), was the most important
gardening book of the 17th century. He described how the
leaves of all types of beetroot could be incorporated into
soups and other dishes and that the roots could be boiled
whole and served with meat. As a point of interest, he
obviously couldn't help using his name in the title as a
sort of linguistic joke (Park in sun). Parkinson was
apothecary to King James I and, later, botanist to

Charles I. He noted several coloured beetroots: white, green, yellow and red, but thought the small red beets, used for their leaves, were descended from the black beet known to the Romans. This red Roman beet was

"the most excellent Beete of all others: his rootes bee as great as the greatest carrot, exceeding red both within and without, very sweet and good, fit to be eaten . . . the Romane red Beete is of much use among cookes . . . and is grown of late dayes into a great custome".

It seems strange nowadays that the very idea of boiling beetroot as a vegetable accompaniment for meat should be so revolutionary. Cooks used them to garnish dishes of meat and fish as a colour point. The newer breeds of leaf beet or chard probably helped in this respect because they come in many coloured forms.

Nicholas Culpeper noted the medical uses of beetroot in his 1653 publication, '*The English Physician or Herball*', but by 1660, when Robert May wrote '*The accomplisht Cook*', beetroot had become a vegetable more widely eaten in England.

BEETROOT IN THE 18TH AND 19TH CENTURIES

During the 19th century beetroot appeared in the lists for vegetable growers in what is the equivalent of seed catalogues today. Varieties such as the *Long Red* and *Long Blood Red* were listed and in the Italian Alps a variety called *Bassano* was developed, named after a nearby town. This was one of the first cylindrical shaped beets. Another variety, grown around Venice, had distinctive red and white rings through it, rather like a target. In Holland a white variety called *Blankoma* was developed and this was quickly followed by many others.

The process of mixing different species of leaf beets and long rooted beets and chards led to a wider range of shapes and sizes across northern Europe. Although only one variety was listed in the USA at the start of the 19th century, by the end several others had been developed, including the *Flat Egyptian* and *Detroit*. This latter variety (no prizes given as to where it came from) arrived in Britain and has been a favourite ever since. It is a small rooted variety and grown for summer salads.

In Britain beetroot was slow to take off at first and was considered a sweet food, hence the discovery of a recipe for crimson biscuits made with beetroot, dating from the 18th century. It was the Victorians who really became entranced with it as a salad vegetable. The Victorians also used it as a rinse for dyeing hair and for fabric dyeing. Up until then, beetroot had been considered a winter crop, with the large rooted varieties dominating because of their good yields. These continued to be grown across central and eastern Europe.

It was discovered that beets were ideal for canning and, during World War II, that beetroot was an ideal vegetable for dehydrating. Since World War II beetroot has been increasingly popular as a pickled vegetable. That would account for my horror of the stuff as a child in the 1960s, I expect.

FODDER BEET
The leaves and the roots of *Beta vulgaris* have been fed to livestock since at least the time of the Romans, but it took until the 18th century before beetroot was specifically grown to provide swollen roots for animals to eat. Where the climate is cooler, the large, white, fleshy varieties have been grown for cattle feed during the winter months.

MANGELWURZELS
I have to admit that, prior to researching this book I thought mangelwurzel referred to some country name for turnips. The band/folk group of the 60s and 70s, known as The Wurzels, sang about cider drinking and agricultural machinery, so I assumed mangels to be a sort of joke, since the songs were of a comic slant. Now I know better!

The name Mangelwurzel comes from the German Mangel/Mangold, 'chard', and Wurzel, 'root'. Mangel-wurzels probably began as a hybrid between yellow beetroot and leaf beet. The first description of a variety grown to be fed to animals came in the late 1700s, when the mangel was being fed to cattle in the Rhineland of Germany. This mangel, a large winter beet, soon became popular across Europe and by the beginning of the 19th century it was also growing in North America. The coarse texture of mangels was too much for consumption by the human palate, except in times of famine, but the roots and leaves were all happily munched on by animals. They were easy to grow, cheap to produce and nutritious into the bargain. After further development of mangels with sugar beet the current fodder crops were produced.

SUGAR BEET

Sugar beet is, commercially, by far the most important form of beetroot. The story of its development is a fairly complicated one, leading right back to the discovery of sugar, so you can read about it in a separate chapter.

The Sugar Trail

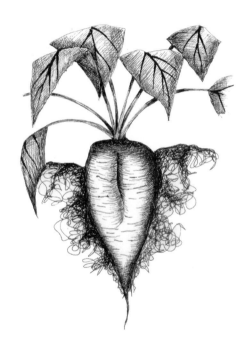

Sugar can be made from various plants, mainly canes and beets, but also the date palm and maple tree. A giant grass containing sweet liquid in the stem was discovered by Polynesians on what are now known as The Solomon Islands in the Pacific, over 5,000 years ago. A legend told of the ancestors of the human race being made from a cane stalk. One bud grew and changed into a man and another grew into a woman.

Sugar was also made in India in ancient times. In Sanskrit, the language of ancient India, the word for sugar, *Sarkara* comes (rather oddly, despite its basic, rough texture) from the word for sand and gravel. The cane was taken to coastal areas, where it remained for many centuries, until in 510 BC Darius, the Emperor of Persia, conquered India and found people eating a sweet substance. Until then the only sweetener known was honey. Other sources suggest that the Greek general, Nearchus, who accompanied Alexander the Great to India in the 4th century BC, told of a reed which produced honey without bees.

When Alexander the Great conquered parts of west Asia he took the 'sacred reed' along with him and before long the Ancient Greeks and the Romans began using sugar as a medicine and luxury food. In the 7th century AD the Arabs invaded Persia and took sugar cane away as part of the spoils of war. The Arabic name for sugar is *Sukkar*, which is obviously connected to the Sanskrit.

A hundred years later sugar cane was growing in Egypt, Greece, Cyprus, North Africa, Syria, Arabic Spain and southern France, before spreading to other parts of Europe. The first Britons to taste sugar were probably soldiers who fought in the Crusades at the beginning of the 12th century. The household of King Henry III was apparently unable to find three pounds of sugar for a banquet in 1226. Even the King couldn't get hold of it. The court was certainly using sugar in 1264, and it formed the basis of trade with Barbary, or Morocco, although it was another 50 years before sugar was available more generally. Even then, it was a luxury which only a few ever tasted and the price was prohibitive. Sugar was so valuable that it was kept in locked caddies. It was dispensed as a sedative and treated more as a medicine than as a food in some places. It remained extremely expensive until at least 1736, when it was apparently listed in the wedding gifts of Maria Theresa, future Queen of Hungary, along with other crystals, ie gems and precious stones.

By the 16th century Venice was the sugar capital of Europe before Antwerp took over. In Italian sugar was called *Zuccero* and, in France, *sucre*. In 1544 there were two sugar refineries in London.

Back in the 15th century the Arabs took sugar to Spain and Portugal. As it was a highly desirable and profitable crop, there was a great need to find new places to grow sugarcane, so when Columbus set sail on his second voyage, in 1493, he took sugar cane to the Caribbean. Crop trials on Santa Domingo were extremely successful and the cane thrived on the fertile soils with heavy rainfall and hotter temperatures. After this event, sugar cane production really took off across the West Indies. Europeans emigrated to the New World to make money across the Caribbean and central and South America. Sugar became known as 'white gold' and the huge workforce to work the plantations came from slaves who were transported from Africa. This new source of sugar didn't go down very well with the European producers, however, and the markets were in turmoil.

When Britain took Jamaica from Spain in 1655 the industry really took off and in 1750 there were 120 refining factories. Sugar was a taxable commodity and by 1815 the government had collected £3 million in revenue. Taxation continued until 1874, when William Gladstone removed the tax. Suddenly sugar was affordable, but this was because there was another source of sugar available, much closer to home. This is where the story takes a turn back to beetroot.

A NEW SOURCE

You may remember that Gerard and his contemporaries commented on the sweetness of the juice extracted from the red roots of beetroot back in the 17th century. Even before that, syrup was extracted on a small scale, but it was during the middle of the 18th century that large white beets were selected for their size and sweetness in Germany and Silesia. A Russian chemist called Andeas Sigismund Marggraf made an important discovery in 1747. He studied the crystals from Silesian beet and discovered that they were exactly the same as those found in sugar cane.

Like many discoveries, it didn't seem worthwhile commercially to produce sugar from beets at first, so it was left to one of Marggraf's students, Franz Carl Achard, to take the idea further. In 1786 he began to grow different beets in his garden, to find out which were the best for sugar extraction. He found that the cone shaped varieties with white skins and roots produced the most sugar. He also found that soil, climate and temperature affected the sugar content. He championed the White Silesian Beet, which became the forerunner of modern sugar beets. In 1799 Achard presented the King of Prussia with a sugar loaf made from sugar beet. His gift was repaid by King Frederick William III giving Achard the money for an estate in Silesia, where he set up a processing factory in 1802, which launched sugar beet as a commercial crop for the first time. By 1810 it was apparent that beet sugar would be a viable industrial concern. A neighbour of Achard, Baron von Koppy, took things a stage further when he found uses for the waste from the beets. These by-products included tops, pulp and molasses for animal fodder, dried pulp as a coffee substitute and alcohol production from molasses to make vinegar.

At the beginning of the 19th century all of Europe's sugar came from cane from the Americas, produced at great human cost, but slave revolts in Santa Domingo showed how insecure the industry could become. With growing unease about the issues of slavery in Europe and about an industry where imports were uncertain, market forces worked against the cane producers and in favour of sugar beet. With the abolition of slavery, production costs rose.

The European sugar beet industry really began because of Napoleon Bonaparte, in France and Belgium. His economic plan for France included measures to reduce imports relying on British colonial trade. Sugar cane was an important import and British naval blockades during the Napoleonic Wars prevented sugar reaching France from West Indian ports. When his army occupied Silesia in 1811, Bonaparte saw the opportunity to, in effect, kill two birds with one stone. He could exploit the discoveries of Achard and end imports of sugar cane. Benjamin Delessert, a French industrialist, received major financial support from Napoleon because of the British blockade. In 1812 he developed the first commercially successful process to extract sugar from sugar beets and by 1814 there were 40 factories in Europe. After the end of the Napoleonic Empire sugar cane made a comeback, but experiments continued in France and Germany. In the 1830s a distinction was finally made between fodder beets, called Runkelrübe and sugar beets, Zuckerrübe. Vilmorin, a plant breeder, discovered that high density roots gave more sugar and then a way of using specific gravity to measure sugar content of the juice. Other inventions helped to measure the sugar content and Vilmorin was able to improve the sugar beet by continually selecting and breeding plants. This meant that production increased again, so that farming of sugar beet in Europe took off and by 1880 beet had become the main source of sugar in Europe. From early days, when only 4–6% sugar was extracted, the figure rose to 18–20%.

Sugar beet made its way to the USA in the 1830s, along with German and French immigrants, who brought new technology with them. Expansion in the beet industry came about in 1900 and by 1990 the USA was producing 8% of the world's sugar beet crop. In 1900 more sugar was produced by beet than cane, but today about two fifths is from beet. The fact that sugar beet thrives in the areas of the world where the demand is highest have contributed greatly to its success. Consumption increased dramatically in the 20th century, hence one of the reasons for the current obesity 'epidemic'.

Sugar beet came later to England, although now it is a major crop in East Anglia. Interest rose in the 1920s, after the end of World War I, when sugar imports were again hit, this time by German U-boat action. The decision was taken by the Government to encourage home production. Once again, sugar supply forced political action to create economic stability.

Around 5,000 beet growers crop a total area of 125,000 hectares. Annual production stands at around seven million tonnes of beet, producing approximately 1 million tonnes of sugar and 500,000 tonnes of animal feed. Sugar beet remains one of the most highly profitable arable crops for UK farmers.

MONOGERM SEED

An important breakthrough for the beet sugar industry came with the development of monogerm beet seed, which when sown with precision drilling equipment, produces well spaced, single, healthy plants. Monogerm seed was sown in the UK in commercial quantities for the first time in 1966, and in 1967 it was sown on 14 per cent of the total acreage. The new seed and the use of weed killers meant it was no longer necessary to hand-hoe the crop and chop out surplus seedlings. This, coupled with mechanisation of sowing and harvesting, meant that gangs of farm labourers in the beet field became a less familiar sight.

The factories' new capabilities were put to the test in the 1960/61 campaign, when a record 7.2 million tons of beet was processed, producing almost 900,000 tons of sugar. By 1980 the UK beet area had expanded from under 190,000 hectares (470,000 acres) to more than 200,000 hectares (495,000 acres).

Sugar has remained a highly taxable commodity and supplied jobs through associated food industries to millions across the globe. Several newly emerging, independent countries have nationalised their industries; such is the potential of sugar production in a growing world population. With concerns over global warming and the limiting of fossil fuels, sucrose as a renewable material and cheap organic chemical produced on a world wide scale could become a major supplier to the plastic and detergent industries. Brazil already grows sugar beet for ethanol production and its uses as a biofuel looks set to continue.

Commercial
Uses of
Beetroot

BEET PIGMENTS

As well as containing valuable nutritional material and conferring health benefits (see pages 57–70), the pigments in beetroot have important commercial uses. First, though, let me explain a bit more about pigments. Plant pigments fall into four categories:

- 1 Chlorophylls
- 2 Carotenoids
- 3 Flavonoids
- 4 Betalains

Just for interest, chlorophyll is the pigment in plants which traps light in photosynthesis, the process by which plants make energy. Chlorophylls are blue green to yellow green, giving most plants their leaf colour.

Carotenoids also trap light energy. The pigment colours are red, orange, yellow and brown, producing many of the autumn colours in plants. They also attract insects to pollinate flowers and give many fruits and vegetables their characteristic colours.

Both these plant pigments are insoluble in water.

Flavonoids are yellow, orange, red and blue pigments and are found in many intensely coloured flowers, fruits and vegetables. They are also present in tea, apples and onions.

Betalain pigments contain nitrogen and give yellow, red, purple, orange and pink colours.

Both flavonoids and betalains are soluble in water and are found in plants where there are vacuoles or spaces within cells, where air, water or other liquids can collect. Most red coloured plants owe their colour to the presence of carotenoids and flavonoids, although red coloured fruits such as strawberries and red grapes and red cabbage varieties get their colour because of anthocyanins, which are quite different. Betalains are restricted to only a few varieties of plants and the only edible varieties are beetroot and prickly pear. Betalains are also found in Fly Agaric, a poisonous mushroom (Amanita muscaria) usually having a red or orange cap with white gills and patches.

MORE ABOUT BETALAINS IN BEETROOT

The betalain pigments were first identified in the red roots of beetroot, which gave its name to these pigments. Betalains are found in greater quantities towards the outside of the root but also exist in the red parts of leaves and stalks. The group is divided into two further categories:

- betacyanin, from which we get betanin
- betaxanthin

Beetroot contains quite a complex mix of betalains, which make it an extremely good food to eat. You can find out more in the nutrition section.

Betanin was discovered in the 1920s and a form of dye was produced in the 1960s. There can be up to 200mg of betanin in one beetroot. Betaxanthins produce yellow pigments. The different colour variations which exist between different varieties of beetroot come about because of the amounts of betanins and betaxanthins occurring. For example, the varieties with deep purple roots contain higher quantities of betanins and the yellow or gold varieties contain more betaxanthins.

The dark and lighter rings visible when you cut a beetroot transversely, ie through the widest part of the root, not from top to bottom, are due to the vacuoles containing different amounts of pigments. This is the reason why beetroots bleed so easily if cut or peeled before cooking.

APPLICATIONS IN FOOD COLOURING

Beetroot pigment is used commercially to dye a range of foods. It is not a very stable dye and changes colour when heated, so it can only be used to dye ice creams, sweets and confectionery. It is cheap to recover and, unlike many artificial colourings, has no known side effects. Beetroot juice has been used for many years: a recipe survives from the late 18th century for pink pancakes. For many years, up until Victorian times, the leaf beet and spinach varieties of *Beta vulgaris* were used to colour sweets green. A cookbook of the 18th century gave a recipe "To make the Crimson Biscuit of red Beet-roots". During the 1860s new artificial pigments replaced many colourings, including beet green, giving much more intense colour. Modern taste uses beetroot to colour tagliatelle, risotto and pink cake icing. It is within the food industry that betalains are still an important natural colouring today and the main source of these is beetroot.

FOOD DYES

For commercial extraction the beets are crushed and the coloured juice is collected and concentrated. The pigment can be provided to food producers as liquid juice concentrate or powder. Freeze drying is used to produce the powders.

Higher levels of concentrate can be acquired by fermentation methods using yeasts. Powders produced this way have a much higher amount of betacyanin than unfermented ones, namely 5–7 times more. The range of colours extracted can be wide and depends on the proportions of betacyanins and betaxanthins in the raw material.

The commercial uses and applications are limited by sensitivity to heat, light and moisture. But betalains are not affected by pH levels between 3.5 and 7.0 (acid to neutral). Between 4.0 and 5.0 they give a bright bluish-red, becoming blue-violet as the pH increases. They won't discolour as a result of acidity, which is why beetroot is such an ideal candidate for pickling in malt vinegar. Above a pH of 7.0 the red dye turns blue. Because of these limitations betalains are used mostly for foods with a low moisture content or short shelf life.

BETANIN

Betanin, known as beetroot red, or E162, is the most important colouring. Unlike many other E numbers, it has no nasty side effects because it is a natural dye. Betanin is a common choice for edible ink, such as that used for marking grades on cuts of meat.
Betanin can be found in the following:
- strawberry ice cream
- frozen desserts
- yoghurt
- tomato pastes and tomato preparations, eg for pizza
- sausages

- cooked ham
- oxtail soup
- bacon burgers
- liquorice
- sauces
- jams
- jellies and gelatine products
- marzipan
- powdered soft drinks
- confectionery e.g. fondants, sugar strands, sugar coatings
- biscuits and cream fillings

ROSY FUTURE

Because of recent food scares and public concerns over synthetic food dyes, including the banned Red Dye number 2 and Sudan 1, the naturally derived dyes like betanin are set to increase in the future. Selective breeding has produced plants with greater pigment content from the average of 130 mg per 100 g of beet to 450–500 mg per 100 g. A variety called Rubin has been identified as having the highest levels of betanin. New technologies could be used in the future to produce beet cells in tissue culture and so increase production further.

STAINS AND VEGETABLE DYES

The disadvantage of beetroot is that it stains easily. Perhaps that's one reason why beetroot has had such a bad press in the past. But betalains are water soluble, so the pigment washes off hands and skin quite easily. Ridding textiles of unwanted stains is only slightly more of a problem. Rinse the clothing as soon as possible in cold water before washing with a detergent. Salt or bicarbonate of soda can also be employed, for example on a tablecloth. They can be sprinkled onto the mark and then brushed off later. Any residual mark can then be treated with warm water.

Beetroot as a natural dye has never been very successful. For example, when I tried to dye fleece for spinning with beetroot, the dye wasn't at all what I had expected. You get a greeny colour with chrome as a mordant, but other attempts (at school) with beetroot dyes have produced pinks and browns. The dyes are not colour fast and fade easily. Now, if someone could make a lasting dye out of beetroot, that really would be a useful addition to natural dyestuffs.

SUGAR BEET PRODUCTION

As we saw in a previous section, the demand for sugar increased with a growing world population. Sugar became a valuable world wide commodity and, as technology improved and economic and political changes came about, its production became cheaper. Producing sugar from beet on your doorstep is always going to rival production halfway across the world — reducing carbon footprints and alleviating fears of intervention from other forces.

ADVANTAGES OF BEET

White beet sugar is made from sugar beets in a single process. The production of sugar from sugar cane is much more involved. Sucrose extraction from beets is easier than with cane for several reasons of which keeping quality and the diffusion process are the two most important. It is not as energy efficient to produce, however, as the cane from sugar cane plants can be used to produce electricity, whereas the pulp from sugar beet will not burn easily. Sugar beet also needs more land than cane sugar, as it is a crop which needs rotating.

CROP ROTATION

The three-year rotation practised by farmers in Europe since the Middle Ages was of a rotation of rye or winter wheat, followed by spring oats or barley, then letting the soil rest (fallow) during the third stage. Suitable rotations made it possible to maintain a productive soil. A four-field rotation was pioneered by farmers in the early 16th century and became a major development of the Agrarian Revolution during the 18th century. The system (wheat, barley, turnips and clover) opened up a fodder crop and grazing crop which meant that animals could be fed throughout the year. It also left the way open for cash crops like sugar beet, when they were developed, to be grown. Today, sugar beet plays an important role as a break crop in the arable rotation. Since pests and diseases are generally different from those of other crops, the cultivation of sugar beet reduces disease and pest levels, which means there is less call for pesticides to be used. Sugar beet also reduces the need for fertilizers for the following cereal crop, by providing residues that break down slowly to release nutrients.

SUGAR BEET

GROWING
Sugar beet production today is a totally mechanised operation with only 50 man-hours per hectare required to grow a typical crop. 30 years ago that figure was 10 times higher. Seed is sown in March and early April. The crop is harvested between mid-September and late February and this is also the period of processing.

PROCESSING
Production starts in autumn, when the beets are removed from the ground. They are transported to a factory where they are weighed and washed. With correct handling and storage, beet will keep for several weeks after harvesting without great loss of sucrose content. It is generally harvested or stored on the farm and delivered to the

factory within 48 hours of harvesting. In countries with very cold winters, however, this time can be much longer. Large ventilated piles can be kept at the factory to avoid process disruptions caused by breaks in harvesting or transport due to weather conditions or low temperatures.

The beets need protection from frost before processing, but left in the ground as a biennial plant sugar beet is expected to survive over winter in order to complete its life cycle. Because the beets have come from the ground they are dirtier than sugar cane, so thorough cleaning and sorting is needed to separate remaining beet leaves, stones and dirt before extraction begins.

Unlike cane extraction, it is important to avoid rupturing the cells of the beet before processing begins because the sucrose will diffuse out of whole cells and the quality of sucrose will be affected.

EXTRACTION
The first stage is to slice the beets into thin chips, which increases the surface area of the beet and makes it easier to extract the sugar. This is done by lifting the beets to the washer, an overflowing tank of water, fitted with propeller paddles. The beets are picked up and sent to a bunker over the slicers, which rotate at 1,000 to 15,000 revolutions per minute. The sliced beets, called cossettes, drop onto a conveyor belt and are taken to the diffuser where the extraction takes place. The cossettes are fed in through the lower end of the inclined diffuser, where they are kept in contact with hot water for about an hour. The temperature of the water is kept at about 73°C (165°F) to avoid growth of bacteria within the diffuser. The cossettes slowly work their way from the lower end to the upper end, being repeatedly squeezed as the water moves in the opposite direction. As the water passes, a stronger sucrose rich juice or solution, along with other chemicals from the flesh of the sugar beet, accumulates at the lower end.

PRESSING
The raw juice can then be drawn off and the pulp is removed from the diffuser. The cossettes are still very

wet and the water in them still holds some useful sugar. They are pressed to squeeze more juice out of them. This juice is used as part of the water in the diffuser and the pressed pulp is sent for drying. This pulp is turned into pellets which will later form an important constituent in animal feeds.

CARBONATATION

The next phase is the cleaning of the raw juice, a process known as carbonatation, whereby small clumps of chalk, or milk of lime, are mixed in the juice. The clumps, as they form, coagulate the impurities and collect the non-sugars. By filtering out the chalk this process also takes out the additional chemicals present. The raw sugar liquid is now ready for sugar production, but is in a very dilute solution, so the next stage of the process is to evaporate the juice. The juice is heated to 82–88°C (180–190°F) in two or three tanks and injected with carbon dioxide from the bottoms of the tanks. Carbonated juice overflows into the next tank in a multi-stage evaporator. In the last tank the carbonated juice and calcium carbonate which have collected are sent to a mud settling tank where clear juice and muddy juice can be separated for further processing.

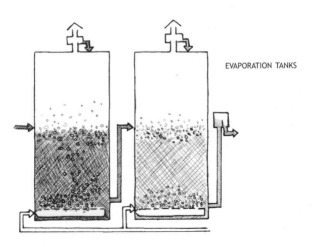

EVAPORATION TANKS

This technique is an efficient way of using steam. Pressure evaporation in the first tank is of 15.5 lb per square inch and the extra vapour is used for heating and boiling in the crystallization process.

BOILING

The thick juice is fed into very large pans, typically holding 60 tons or more of sugar syrup. In the pan even more water is boiled off until conditions are right for sugar crystals to grow on the continuously fed juice. Once the crystals have grown, the mixture of crystals and molasses is spun in centrifuges to separate the two. The crystals of raw sugar are then given a final dry with hot air before being packed. The molasses or treacle is a thick syrup by-product. It undergoes further refining and extraction of sugar before it is finished. Beet molasses are usually turned into cattle food or sent to a distillery where industrial alcohol is made. It is not of the same quality as cane molasses so cannot be made into rum.

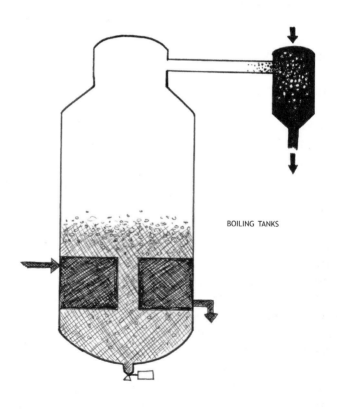

BOILING TANKS

SUGAR TYPES AND GRADES

A typical raw juice from diffusion will contain 14% sugar and the residual pulp will contain 1% to 2%. The final sugar is white and ready for use, whether in the domestic or commercial market. British Sugar produces more than 1 million tonnes of sugar from beet each year at a rate of about nine tonnes of sugar per hectare. It takes about eight beets to make one kilo of sugar. Sugar is used in the manufacture of products in the following industries:

- cereals
- confectionery
- drinks
- ice-cream and other dairy products
- pharmaceutical products
- bakeries
- preserves, condiments, sauces and canned goods

These are some of the main grades available:

WHITE GRANULATED
Most sugar is consumed as white granulated, classified by grain size. Within this classification grain size may vary between 1.0 mm (0.04 in) and 0.25 mm (less than 0.01 in). Coarse-grained sugars, such as sanding sugar, are used for decorating biscuits and desserts. Normal granulated sugars for table use have a grain size of about 0.5 mm (0.08 inches).

CASTER
Finer grades result from sieving the granulated sugar. Caster sugar (0.35 mm) is used in baking. Superfine sugar, also called Baker's sugar, berry sugar, or bar sugar in the USA, is used for sweetening drinks or for preparing meringues. This type gets its name from a caster, which was a container with a perforated top to shake pepper. Fine grained sugar became known as caster sugar because it was suitable for use in a caster. My grandma had one, made of glass with a silver top. It was brought out on occasions such as when we were having strawberries and cream, so that you could dust the fruit with caster sugar.

COFFEE
Coffee sugar consists of large brown crystals which are produced as granules in repeated boilings from liquor of the desired colour.

ICING SUGAR
This is produced by milling sugar crystals and adding cornflour to prevent caking or lumping. Icing sugar dissolves very quickly, making it ideal for decorating cakes.

CUBE
This is produced by pressing and moulding granulated sugar, with liquid sugar to fix the crystals together like a sort of cement. Sugar cubes were invented in the 1840s. In France this is the most common way of adding sugar to coffee, and cube sugar sales are high.

LIQUID SUGAR
This is produced in two grades, liquid sucrose and liquid invert. Invert is a mixture of equal parts of glucose and fructose. It is found naturally in fruits and honey and produced artificially for use in the food industry.

CANDY SUGAR
This is used mainly by the brewing industry. The large white crystals are obtained by slow crystallization of very high quality liquor.

BROWN
Brown sugar is white sugar which is then combined with molasses to give a softer texture. The presence of molasses does not change sugar's nutritional value. Brown sugar is marketed as light and dark varieties: the lighter the brown sugar, the more delicate the flavour will be. Brown sugar is not the same as raw sugar, which is the residue left after sugar cane has been processed, to remove the molasses and refine the sugar crystals.

OTHER BY-PRODUCTS OF SUGAR BEET PRODUCTION

BEET FODDER

The pulp from sugar beet production can be fed to animals wet or dry. The wet pulp can be consumed directly from the factory where the sugar is produced. Most is dried, however, in rotary driers and then stored. When dry the protein content is about 9%.

BEET MOLASSES

- Molasses can be fed to livestock or added to beet pulp.
- They are used to make Monosodium glutamate. This is a white crystalline flavour enhancer, used widely across the world. It was originally produced from seaweed but the two main sources of raw material are now wheat glutens and de-sugared molasses from sugar beet production. Monosodium glutamate is used in the preparation of canned and dried soups and also in the production of meat, vegetable, fowl, and fish products.
- Some European beet molasses are used to manufacture citric acid by fermentation.

TOMATOES

British Sugar is the UK's largest grower of salad tomatoes. A site covers an area of 5 hectares and produces over 34 million tomatoes each year between April and November. The greenhouses are heated from the energy produced in the production of sugar.

BIOFUELS

Biofuels are made from renewable raw materials, such as wheat or sugar beet, which are added to conventional fuels. They help to reduce overall emissions of green-house gases and other exhaust pollutants and are a sustainable alternative to fossil fuels. Bioalcohols are made from the fermentation of starches or sugars. They are usually blended with petrol but can also be used with diesel.

The Nutritional Value of Beetroot and Chard

Packed into every portion of beetroot or chard is a whole variety of minerals and vitamins, which help keep our bodies running properly by providing the raw material for a range of functions and preventing disease.

Our bodies need minerals and vitamins every day to function properly. Some vitamins which are fat soluble can be stored in the liver, but other, water soluble varieties need to be consumed regularly, as the body cannot store them.

Here are the main 'goodies' present in varieties of *beta vulgaris:*

VITAMIN A

Vitamin A is a group of compounds that play an important role in vision, bone growth, reproduction and cell growth. It helps to regulate the immune system, preventing or fighting off infections by making white blood cells that destroy harmful bacteria and viruses. Vitamin A promotes healthy surface linings to the eyes, respiratory, urinary, and intestinal tracts. When those linings break down, it becomes easier for bacteria to enter the body and cause infection. Vitamin A also helps the skin and mucous membranes function as a barrier to bacteria and viruses.

BETA CAROTENE
The Vitamin A that is found in colourful fruits and vegetables is a carotenoid (remember the pigments described in the earlier section?). Chard contains beta-carotene, which, once eaten, converts into vitamin A. While excessive amounts of vitamin A in supplement form can be toxic, the body will only convert as much vitamin A from beta-carotene as it needs. This feature makes beta-carotene (and chard in particular) a safe source of Vitamin A. If you are a smoker, or are frequently subjected to passive smoking, regular intake of Vitamin A could be essential to staying healthy. You can read more later in this section.

THE VITAMIN B GROUP

VITAMIN B1 THIAMIN

Thiamin is one of a group of water-soluble vitamins that participate in many of the chemical reactions in the body. Thiamin helps the body cells convert carbohydrates into energy. It is also essential for the functioning of the heart, muscles, and nervous system. Vegetables like chard and leaf beets are not very high in thiamin, but when consumed in large amounts, they can become a significant source.

A deficiency of thiamin can cause weakness, fatigue, psychosis, and nerve damage. A high consumption of alcohol makes it hard for the body to absorb thiamin from foods. This can lead to a disease called beriberi.

VITAMIN B2 RIBOFLAVIN

Riboflavin has a number of important functions. It helps keep skin, eyes, the nervous system and mucous membranes healthy. It may help the body absorb iron from the food we eat and it helps produce steroids and red blood cells.

VITAMIN B6 PYRIDOXINE

Allows the body to use and store energy from carbohydrates and protein, as well as helping to form haemoglobin.

VITAMIN BC FOLATE

Folic acid is known as folate in its natural form. If you are intending to become pregnant — or are pregnant already — you should take a daily supplement from the time you stop using contraception until the 12th week of pregnancy. Folates are also used to treat anaemia.

VITAMINS B7, B3 AND B5 BIOTIN, NIACIN AND PANTOTHENIC ACID

Biotin, niacin and pantothenic acid all help the body turn the food we eat into energy. Niacin also helps keep the nervous and digestive systems healthy.

VITAMIN C

Vitamin C is the main water-soluble antioxidant in the body and is vital for the healthy functioning of the immune system. It is good at preventing common colds and may also help to reduce recurrent ear infections. Vitamin C helps Vitamin E become active and is associated with reducing inflammation caused by asthma and arthritis. It is also particularly effective in combating free-radical formation caused by pollution and cigarette smoke.

VITAMIN E

Vitamin E is the body's main fat-soluble antioxidant. It plays a big role in preventing cardio vascular disease and is one of the main antioxidants found in cholesterol. It helps prevent free radicals that would damage the cell membranes by oxidizing the cholesterol. If cholesterol is oxidized it causes problems by sticking to blood vessel walls and blocking arteries.

VITAMIN K

Vitamin K is responsible for maintaining healthy bones. It activates osteocalcin, which is a major bone protein. A portion of cooked chard or spinach contains well beyond your daily recommended intake, but as it is fat soluble you don't need to have it every day. Any of the vitamin your body doesn't need immediately is stored in the liver for future use. Vitamin K has other important functions, for example, helping wounds to heal properly by clotting the blood.

MINERALS

MAGNESIUM
Helps to regulate the nerve and muscle tone. Magnesium keeps the muscles relaxed by preventing calcium entering the nerve cells. Insufficient magnesium may lead to muscle spasms or cramps, migraine, high blood pressure and fatigue.

CALCIUM
Both magnesium and calcium are needed for healthy bones. Calcium is essential for the normal growth and maintenance of bones and teeth. Requirements must be met throughout life, with long-term calcium deficiency leading to an increasing occurrence of osteoporosis, particularly amongst women over 50, in which bones deteriorate and there is an increased risk of fractures.

MANGANESE
Manganese is an essential mineral trace element. Its name comes from the Greek word for magic. Manganese is an antioxidant that is important in the breakdown of amino acids and the production of energy. It activates various enzymes which are important for proper digestion of foods. It helps break down cholesterol and feeds the nerves and brain. It is necessary for normal skeletal development, maintaining sex hormone production, and for regulating blood sugar levels.

POTASSIUM
Potassium helps to contract all the muscles in the body. It is essential for heart function and maintaining normal blood pressure. Studies have shown that potassium reduces blood pressure and the risk of strokes.

IRON
Chard is a valuable vegetable source of iron, which is found in every cell in the body. Iron links with protein to form haemoglobin, which is the oxygen transporter in your blood. Iron keeps your immune system healthy and helps to produce energy. Insufficient iron leads to anaemia. You can read about the 'Popeye' connection later in this chapter.

COPPER
Copper is another essential trace mineral present in all body tissues. Along with iron it helps in the formation of red blood cells. It also helps in keeping the blood vessels, nerves, immune system, and bones healthy. Dark leafy greens, like chard and spinach, are a good source of copper in the diet.

PHOSPHOROUS

Phosphorus is a mineral that makes up 1% of the total body weight. It is present in every cell of the body, but 85% of the body's phosphorus is found in the bones and teeth. It plays an important role in the body's use of carbohydrates and fats and in the synthesis of protein for the growth, maintenance, and repair of cells and tissues. It is also crucial for the production of a molecule the body uses to store energy. Phosphorus works with the B vitamins. It assists in the contraction of muscles, in kidney function, in maintaining the regularity of the heartbeat, and in nerve conduction. The main food sources are the protein food groups of meat and milk but there are small quantities in green vegetables. A meal plan that provides adequate amounts of calcium and protein also provides an adequate amount of phosphorus.

SODIUM

Sodium is an element that the body needs to function properly and occurs naturally in most foods. The body uses sodium to regulate blood pressure and blood volume. Sodium is also critical for the functioning of muscles and nerves. Beets and celery naturally contain sodium, as does drinking water, although the amount varies depending on the source.

ZINC

Zinc is second only to iron in its concentration in the body. The body needs zinc for the immune system to work properly. It plays a role in cell division, cell growth, wound healing, and the breakdown of carbohydrates. Zinc is also needed for the senses of smell and taste. Most zinc is consumed through high protein foods such as meat and fish. Low-protein diets and vegetarian diets tend to be low in zinc, so eating chard, which contains zinc, will help offset any shortfall.

SELENIUM

Selenium is present as a trace element. It may help prevent cancer by acting as an antixodant.

FOOD GROUPS

With all these minerals and vitamins packed into the roots and the leaves of beetroot, perpetual spinach and chard, there's the added bonus of few calories, good dietary fibre and protein, virtually no fat and no cholesterol.

In 225 grams (8 oz) of sliced beetroot there are approximately:

Calories	36
Carbohydrate	8.5 g
Protein	1.5 g
Dietary fibre	1.5 g
Phosphorus	32 mg
Potassium	259 mg
Folate	53.2 mcg (micrograms)

Most of the carbohydrate in beetroot is sugar, making it a potentially tricky food for diabetics. However, the advice I've been given is that no foods are banned entirely, and given the benefits of beetroot in terms of fibre, vitamins and minerals, I eat beetroot about once a week. Raw beetroot contains slightly less sugar than boiled beetroot, while pickled beetroot contains a fair bit less. The sugar content is hardly surprising, considering that sugar beet was bred from beetroot, but beetroot does have more carbohydrate than most other vegetables. Potassium and phosphorus are vital minerals, as described above, and beetroot has a higher amount of folate than most other vegetables.

In one cup (175 g or 5 oz) of cooked chard there are approximately:

Calories	35
Carbohydrates	7 g
Protein	3 g
Dietary fibre	3.68 g
Calcium	102 mg
Iron	4 mg
Magnesium	151 mg

Phosphorus	58 mg
Potassium	960 mg
Sodium	313 mg
Vitamin C	32 mg
Folate	15 mcg

The way that you cook or prepare beetroot has quite a significant effect on its nutritional value. Boiled beetroot is particularly high in potassium, calcium and magnesium. Raw beet has five times more phosphorous than pickled beetroot, but if you boil your beetroot you will have even more benefit. Chlorine levels are much higher in pickled beetroot due to the presence of acetic acid. The iron content of beetroot is comparable to other vegetables and it doesn't live up to its image as a high iron food to combat anaemia.

COMPARISON OF FOOD VALUES FOR BEETROOT AND CHARD PER 100g

	RAW BEETROOT	BOILED BEETROOT	PICKLED BEETROOT	CHARD
CALORIES	36	46	28	35
CARBOHYDRATE	7.6 g	9.5 g	5.6 g	8.5 g
PROTEIN	1.7 g	2.3 g	1.2 g	3 g
WATER	87 g	82 g	89 g	88 g

The advice to eat at least five portions of fruit and vegetables per day is now well advertised. One portion of beetroot would be three baby beets or about seven slices of beetroot. However, more specific advice suggests that leafy vegetables and those with strong colours should play a greater part. Beetroot as a nutritious vegetable fits the bill entirely. There are very strong health reasons for doing so, as you will find out if you read on. The different phases of the human life cycle impose extra requirements of our bodies and that often means changing our diet to compensate.

MMM THESE COLOURS TASTE YUMMY!

Much has been written about a rainbow approach to healthy eating, with red, orange and green fruits and vegetables, along with yellow, blue and purple varieties offering all the nutrients you need to grow and stay healthy. This is because it has been recognized that plants with strong pigments also contain many other nutrients. The carotenoid pigments all act as antioxidants and beetroot is full of carotenoids. The leaves of beet varieties, like spinach beet and chard, are full of chlorophyll, another of the plant pigments. As well as its role in providing plants with energy, chlorophyll also has antioxidant properties. The darker the green, the more chlorophyll there is present.

The following chart shows the vitamins and minerals present in 175 g (5 oz) of chard or spinach leaves in relation to the recommended daily consumption:

NUTRIENT	% OF RECOMMENDED DAILY INTAKE	STAR RATING	NOTES
Vitamin K	716	★ ★ ★	Can be stored in the liver
Vitamin A	110	★ ★ ★	Can be stored
Vitamin C	53	★ ★ ★	Cannot be stored
Vitamin E	17	★ ★ ★	Can be stored
Vitamin B Thiamin	4	★ ★	
Riboflavin	9		
Niacin	3	★	
Pantothenic acid	3	★	

Pyridoxine	8	★ ★	
Folate	4	★	
Biotin	4	★	
Dietry fibre	15	★ ★ ★	
Protein	7	★ ★	
Iron	22	★ ★ ★	
Magnesium	38	★ ★ ★	
Manganese	29	★ ★ ★	
Potassium	27	★ ★ ★	
Copper	15	★ ★	
Calcium	10	★ ★	
Phosphorus	6	★	
Tryptophan	9	★ ★	amino acid essential in nutrition
Zinc	4	★	
Sodium		★ ★	

Key to ratings   ★ ★ ★ excellent   ★ ★ very good   ★ good

CAUTION

As well as watching your intake of beetroot if you are diabetic, you should also avoid giving it to young children. Beetroot has been shown to contain more nitrate than most vegetables, although home grown ones probably contain less than cultivated varieties. Nitrate is not harmful but, on storage, it may change and cause vomiting and diarrhoea in infants, if eaten in high amounts.

Swiss chard is among a small number of foods that contain measurable amounts of oxalates. When these become too concentrated in body fluids, they can crystallize and cause health problems, so if you already have untreated kidney or gallbladder problems it might be best to avoid eating Swiss chard.

Another possible side effect of eating too much beetroot is beeturia. Some people have more acid in their stomachs than others. When you have eaten some beetroot, it can make your urine pink, of even red. This has frequently led people into thinking that there is something seriously wrong, when it is only the pigment from the beetroot that has not been absorbed.

Health Benefits Throughout History

In mythology, Aphrodite is said to have eaten beets to retain her beauty. Who can tell? If she did eat beetroot or the leaves of spinach beet, then there's every possibility that the vitamins and minerals did the trick.

Various cultivated forms of beetroot have been used for medicinal purposes since ancient times. Hippocrates spoke of the use of beet leaves as binding and dressings for wounds. He used beets after the treatment of ulcers or abscesses. He believed that juice from the leaf bindings would aid healing. The Romans used beetroot as a treatment for fevers and constipation. Of five recorded recipes for soups to be given as a laxative, three included beetroot. The Romans used beetroot juice as an aphrodisiac. It contains boron, so there might be something in that.

EARS, EYES AND NOSES
From the Middle Ages, people used beetroot to treat a variety of conditions, especially illnesses relating to digestion and the blood. If you have read the History section you'll remember Platina, in the 15th century, recommending taking beetroot with garlic to freshen the breath. I also mentioned John Gerard and his Herball. He recommended that to reduce catarrh you should boil white beet roots and, somehow, put it up your nostrils. This would 'draw forth flegme, and purgeth the head'. A bit later Nicholas Culpeper suggested using red beetroot juice up your nose to 'purgeth the head, helpeth the noise in the ears, and the toothache'. Bargain! Three for one offer! Just for good measure he threw in the fact that it cured bad breath and that if you applied juice to the temples it helped eye inflammation. I think we could safely say he was a fan of the new beetroot varieties of his time.

STOMACHS AND DIGESTION
Beetroot juice or broth had been recommended for the aged, weak or infirm since the Middle Ages, as it was thought to be easily digested, but in the 17th century John Parkinson advocated using the leaves of beets 'to mollify and open the belly'. The white roots, cleaned and 'mixed with a little honey and salt, will provoke stools if

rubbed on the belly'. Culpeper really was a fan: 'White Beet doth much loosen the belly, and is of a cleansing and digesting quality and provoketh urine. The juice of it openeth obstructions both of the liver and spleen'. We'll look at modern research a bit later in this section.

BLOOD

I'm beginning to wonder if Culpeper had shares in a beetroot farm. There seem to be no limits to his recommendations. He advocated its use for a whole range of ailments, many of which have been investigated scientifically since. By his day, beetroot had long been recommended to treat menstrual problems. Culpeper wrote that 'red beet is good to stay the bloody flux, woman's courses and the whites, and to help the yellow jaundice'. By 'courses' he meant periods. Modern medicine and research has found that the relatively high levels of iron and manganese in beetroot and spinach help to ease problems caused by heavy bleeding, which, of course, lowers the haemoglobin levels in the blood and can cause anaemia.

BONES, BURNS, WOUNDS AND BITES

Since Anglo-Saxon times the juice extracted from *Beta vulgaris* roots has been used to treat broken bones and as a treatment for wounds and bites. Culpeper used the juice of white beet as a balm for burns. He also said it was good for all wounds, blisters, and skin disorders. White beet leaves boiled and laid on chilblains apparently cures them. I can't say I've ever had the need to try this, but Culpeper also suggested making a skin balm with beet in water and some vinegar to heal itches. Vinegar has long been used as a bath for skin problems and a whole range of health benefits: enough to fill a book!

SKIN AND HAIR

Decoctions were also recommended. They were said to cure dandruff, scurf, scabs, running sores, ulcers and 'cankers in the head, legs, or other parts, and is much commended against baldness and shedding of the hair'. To do this you had to boil the roots until the liquid reduced by about a third. This broth was then strained and the liquid was drunk. Most of these ideas don't stand up to today's more scientific herbal remedies, although beetroot juice is still recommended to ease piles or haemorrhoids. Ouch!

SNAKE BITE?

Culpeper records that beetroot juice is effective against all venomous creatures. There is no known benefit in beetroot which will counteract snake venom, but I suppose if there was nothing else to try, it had to be your best shot.

POPEYE'S POINT

Have you ever wondered why Popeye ate spinach? Back in the 1930s Popeye's creator, Max Fleisher, was looking around for a special food to give the character special powers and strength. About ten years earlier a report had suggested that spinach was exceptionally rich in iron, calcium and Vitamins A and C. This information was based on the work of E von Wolf, dating from 1870. The mineral and vitamin content of spinach is no different in this respect from other *Beta vulgaris* species and even comes from the same family of plants (Chenopodiaceae). Anyway, the popularity of the cartoon character was responsible for a twenty fold increase in production. When von Wolf's work was looked at again in 1937, someone discovered that a decimal point had been put in the wrong place originally, and that spinach only contained a tenth of the iron originally claimed. Most of the iron and calcium in spinach is bound to oxalic acid (not a nutrient) and can't be used by the human body anyway. Still, this misplaced claim (or decimal point) did nothing to diminish Popeye's popularity, and even though the claim was proved false, it doesn't detract from the other, overwhelming benefits gained from eating spinach. It's a shame it didn't do the business for beetroot and chard as well. Perhaps someone needs to invent a new superhero, dependent on beetroot juice, or a nice beetroot salad, lightly dressed with oil and vinegar!

MODERN BENEFITS OF BEETROOT AND CHARD

GENERAL HEALTH
Nobody can say that beetroot is a cure for cancer or any other disease. However, it clearly has significant benefits towards maintaining general good health and as a preventative step in fending off the effects of the lives we lead today. The five a day guide is only the start, really. If we are sensible about eating the right amounts of fruit and vegetables, in conjunction with regular exercise and avoiding smoking, over consumption of alcohol or other substances, then there's still no cast iron guarantee that we will avoid disease, just as there's no guarantee that we'll win the lottery. I'm a Type II diabetic, who has never smoked, been overweight, consumed excessive amounts of alcohol (not regularly, anyway) and exercised regularly in younger days. For the moment I control the diabetes through diet and exercise, and I want to keep it that way as long as possible. Diabetes doesn't even appear to be in the family genes, so sometimes there's no explanation. I do consume regular portions of root vegetables, green vegetables, spinach and, now, beetroot, and so far, so good. I need a high fibre diet to keep blood sugar levels under control, and beetroot and spinach are excellent vegetables for people with diabetes.

The Romans drank glasses of beetroot juice for their health, so why not today? A daily glass of beetroot juice is one of the recommended methods to lower the risk of developing cancer. Beetroot is available as a powdered preparation. This is made without subjecting the beets to high temperatures that would degrade minerals and vitamins. Freeze dried beetroot, and beetroot crisps (delicious, but very sweet) are also available.

CANCER TREATMENT

FREE RADICALS AND ANTIOXIDANTS

Free radicals cause damage to cells by attacking molecules for their electrons. Once damaged, a molecule becomes a free radical itself. Antioxidants neutralise free radicals by donating one of their own electrons, without becoming unstable themselves. Instead, they act as scavengers, cleaning up and helping to prevent cell damage that could lead to disease. Some free radicals arise normally, when the body's immune system's cells purposefully create them to neutralise viruses and bacteria. Environmental factors such as pollution, radiation, cigarette smoke and herbicides can also create free radicals. It is important to note that free radical damage intensifies as we get older, so eating foods high in Vitamin C and E and betanin and also those high in fibre can only do good. Many studies have noted high vitamin C intakes with low rates of cancer, particularly cancers of the mouth, larynx and oesophagus.

Over the centuries broths including beetroot and poultices of beet have apparently been used to treat tumours of the intestines, head, legs, genitals and rectum. Beetroot has also been used to treat lung cancer, prostate cancer, breast cancer and leukaemia, although many reports are unsubstantiated. Modern interest in beetroot as a treatment for cancer dates from around 1930, when two German doctors used beetroot to treat cancer patients. In 1939, a Hungarian scientist carried out experiments on patients with cancers and observed improvements in their general condition. In the 1950s another Hungarian doctor, Alexander Ferenczi, developed a radical treatment using only beetroot juice to treat patients suffering from a range of cancers. This involved drinking one litre of beetroot juice per day for at least three months. The research suggested this treatment was based on beetroot containing anthocyanins, the pigment in red cabbage, but as we saw in a previous section, the red pigment in beetroot is due to betalains.

Beetroot does, however, contain several suspected anti-cancer properties, including the alkaloid allantoine, shown to have an anti-tumour effect in the 1960s by a Romanian, Constantinescu. Later work has confirmed this effect and it is now thought that the combined effects of betanin, allantoine, vitamin C and other compounds present have a beneficial effect.

Allantoine is an extract also found in the comfrey plant. It is used for its healing, soothing, and anti-irritating properties. Allantoine helps to heal wounds and skin irritations and stimulate growth of healthy tissue. It is also used in products treating acne, sun care products, and clarifying lotions because of its ability to help heal minor wounds and promote healthy skin.

Betanin is the most common betalain in red beets. It is known to inhibit a wide range of oxidative reactions that have negative effects in the body. Betaxanthins, as described in the Commercial Uses section, are the yellowy betalain pigments in beetroot. They also create antiradical activity. Betanin is absorbed easily in the gut, with very little being excreted under normal conditions. You don't need to eat much beetroot for its high antioxidant properties to start doing good.

The fibre in chard and perpetual spinach is another cancer preventing bonus. Fibre prevents cancer causing chemicals from harming cells lining the colon. Added to the effects of Vitamins C and E in disarming free radicals, you've already got a pretty strong team working for you if you eat enough fibre.

Beta-carotene, which is present in chard and leaves of spinach beet, has also been the subject of extensive research in relationship to cancer prevention and the prevention of oxygen-based damage to cells. Consumption of beta carotene, one of the carotenoid pigments, has been studied in connection with the incidence of skin cancer in Australia. In population surveys amongst men, researchers found that those who ate more foods rich in beta-carotene had a lower statistical risk of developing skin cancer.

A HEALTHY HEART

SOME OF THE CAUSES OF HEART DISEASE

Cholesterol is a substance found among the lipids (fats) in the bloodstream and in all the cells of the body. It is an important part of a healthy body and is used to form cell membranes and some hormones, but a high level of cholesterol in the blood is a major risk factor for coronary heart disease, leading to heart attack. Cholesterol and other fats cannot dissolve in the blood. They have to be transported to and from the cells by special carriers called lipoproteins, the main ones being low-density lipoprotein (LDL), often referred to as bad cholesterol and high-density lipoprotein (HDL). If too much LDL circulates it can build up in the walls of the arteries and clog them. This condition is known as atherosclerosis.

A clot that forms near plaque that builds up can block the blood flow to part of the heart muscle and cause a heart attack. A stroke results if a clot blocks the blood flow to part of the brain. HDL cholesterol is known as good cholesterol because a high HDL level seems to protect against heart attack.

The liver makes all the cholesterol that the body needs, so people don't need to consume it in food, but unfortunately food from an animal source, including dairy goods, contains cholesterol. Plants do not, so beetroot is a source of only good things for your body. Help is at hand through the benefits of Vitamin E, which plays an important role in the prevention of cardiovascular disease.

THE ROLE OF VITAMIN E

Vitamin E travels throughout the body neutralising free radicals that would otherwise damage cell membranes, brain cells, and cholesterol.

Vitamin E is one of the main antioxidants found in cholesterol particles and helps prevent free radicals from oxidizing cholesterol, which can only stick to blood vessel walls after it has been oxidized. Getting plenty of Vitamin E can reduce the risk of developing atherosclerosis.

BETAINE

Betaine is a nutrient found in beetroot. Betaine supplements are manufactured as a by-product of sugar beet processing and are prescribed to patients to lower levels of homocysteine that can be harmful to blood vessels. This reduces the risk of developing heart disease, stroke, and vascular disease. Betaine has other important properties, described later in this chapter.

PROTECT WITH POTASSIUM

Potassium is an important electrolyte. Electrolytes are involved in nerve transmission and the contraction of all muscles, including the heart. Electrolyte balance is regulated by hormones, generally with the kidneys flushing out excess levels. Muscle contraction is dependent upon the presence of key electrolytes calcium, sodium, and potassium. Without sufficient levels of these minerals muscle weakness or severe muscle contractions may occur. Potassium is essential for maintaining normal blood pressure and heart function. Beetroot and the leaves of spinach and chard are excellent sources of potassium. Studies of a large sample of men in the USA over four years showed that those who ate foods rich in potassium, magnesium and fibre had lower blood pressure and a considerably lower risk of stroke.

A TONIC FOR THE HEART AND BLOOD

For a long time people assumed that the red colour of beetroot meant that it was good for the blood and for circulation. Although the actual colour is not directly related there are a number of ways in which beetroot and chard help. As well as potassium, which helps with blood pressure the roots and leaves of the beetroot family contain iron and folic acid. Haemoglobin, the red pigment in the red blood cells is responsible for transporting oxygen around the body and iron is an essential mineral in the formation of haemoglobin. Folic acid has been shown to have a positive effect on some types of anaemia, so beetroot acts as a tonic, as well as other important functions explained later.

OTHER CONDITIONS WHICH MAY BE HELPED BY EATING BEETROOT

ASTHMA, OSTEOARTHRITIS, AND RHEUMATOID ARTHRITIS

Vitamin E has significant anti-inflammatory effects that result in the reduction of symptoms in asthma, osteoarthritis, and rheumatoid arthritis, conditions where free radicals and inflammation play a big role. Likewise, Vitamin C has been shown to reduce the free radical damage which leads to severe inflammation. Unlike Vitamin E, Vitamin C cannot be stored so needs to be consumed daily.

HIV/AIDS

We have seen how the minerals and vitamins in beetroot have been shown to prevent illness by bolstering the immune system. It is believed that people living with the HIV retrovirus that causes Aids (acquired immune deficiency syndrome) can delay the onset of Aids through an active lifestyle and sound nutrition as well as medicines. Foods that include antioxidants are particularly recommended, along with foods rich in vitamins. Beetroot, along with garlic and ginger are particularly noted for their health benefits, taken alongside anti-retroviral drugs.

SMOKING AND LOSS OF VITAMIN A

Sadly, some of my best friends are heavy smokers. Happily, they seem to be remarkably fit and healthy. Perhaps they are just lucky, although maybe it is due to the diet they consume. As a long term vegetarian Andy has always eaten large quantities of green vegetables and fish. Some studies suggest that cigarette smoke causes a deficiency of Vitamin A, but that a diet rich in Vitamin A can help counter the effects. The younger you start to smoke, the more likely you are to become deficient in Vitamin A. So if you have to put up with a smoker in the house, as a passive smoker you can do yourself and your children a favour and eat foods like beetroot and chards, which are rich in Vitamin A. We only let our friends smoke in the garden (next door...)

FOLIC ACID AND PREGNANCY
Beetroot is an excellent source of folic acid. Both the greens (chard and perpetual spinach) and roots of beetroot are recommended for women who are planning to get pregnant, because they provide a good source of folic acid as well as other vitamins and minerals. Folic acid is a vitamin that functions as a carrier of carbon units and is essential for the synthesis of compounds which play an important role in developmental processes. As well as beetroot (raw is best), there are a lot of folates in other green-leaf vegetables, liver and kidneys. Taking folic acid supplements before the start of pregnancy has been shown to reduce the incidence of spina bifida in babies. So, like some recent celebrity mothers-to-be who have advocated eating beetroot, it isn't just necessarily a fad or food craving. You need to eat the beetroot raw or boiled for optimum folic acid benefit, as pickled beetroot contains virtually none.

DEPRESSION AND BETAINE
Depression is closely linked to neurotransmitters in the brain not functioning properly. Low levels of serotonin affect a range of physiological processes that result in depression. One approach to treatment is through diet. Betaine is one of a number of compounds in foods which have been shown to raise serotonin levels and create a calming effect in patients and modify mood. Betaine is a nitrogenous compound found in beetroot. It has become a valuable by-product of sugar beet processing, where it is extracted from beet juice. Beetroot is therefore a good mood food, alongside ginseng and foods containing caffeine and tryptophan. It is sold as a white powder.

THE EFFECTS OF ALCOHOL
Betaine promotes the regeneration of liver cells and helps the conversion of fats, so betaine may also be an effective treatment for liver failure brought on by alcohol abuse. Betaine has also been used as treatment for a type of hepatitis, kidney disorder, and antherosclerosis, but more research is needed in this area. A side effect of taking betaine as a supplement is body odour, but if it treats your needs I expect you would put up with that.

SKIN AND DAMAGE FROM UV RAYS
Research into nutrition is discovering the role of various foods which improve the resilience of your skin against UV damage. This reduces your risk of sunburn and various skin cancers. 13 nutrients have been identified which increase the skin's protection. Ten of these are found in spinach and chard.

BEETROOT AS AN APHRODISIAC
It has been suggested in ancient folklore that if a woman and man eat from the same beet, they will fall in love. Beetroot doesn't look much like the sort of food you associate with aphrodisiacal qualities, but throughout history it has had its moments. The Romans certainly revered it and it is thought beetroot juice may have been drunk at some so-called orgies. Beetroot is a rich source of boron, which plays a role in the production of human sex hormones.

Field-marshal Viscount Montgomery, famous for the victory at El Alamein during the Second World War, encouraged his soldiers to 'find favours in the beetroot fields'. By this he is understood to have meant consorting with prostitutes. That certainly gives rise to a new twist on 'The Full Monty'!

OTHER BEETROOT HERBAL REMEDIES AND PREVENTIONS

Ancient civilizations and herbalists prescribed *Beta vulgaris* for a number of medical conditions. Science has provided support for some traditional beetroot remedies, whereas some medicinal properties of beets have been dismissed or described as having little value. Since the 1930s beetroot has enjoyed a revival as a treatment for modern diseases, especially cancer.

Here are a few ideas for more modern herbal remedies. They look remarkably like some of Culpeper's ideas to me. I can't say I've tried them, but pass them on for interest. As always, seek professional advice if you are in doubt.

FOR BOILS, SKIN INFLAMMATION, PIMPLES AND PUSTULES

Boil white beet roots and leaves. When cooled, discard the roots and tops and apply the water used to the affected area.

IRRITABLE SKIN, MEASLES, FEVERS

This may be worth a try, if you've just boiled some beets anyway. Sponge down with three parts beet water to one part white vinegar.

AS A HAIR WASH FOR TREATMENT AGAINST DANDRUFF OR SCURF

Use the water cooled from boiling up beetroot to rinse the hair and scalp. The Victorians used this for a light colouring rinse.

RESTORATIVE TREATMENT AFTER ILLNESS

Juice one medium beetroot (raw), one to two apples and three medium carrots. I'm assuming this will be blended and water added to thin a little. Add a teaspoonful of lime juice to increase its medicinal value. See below for more information based on medical research.

GASTRIC ULCER

Take fresh beet juice mixed with a tablespoonful of honey every morning before breakfast.

KIDNEYS AND GALL BLADDER

Beetroot is said to support and stimulate the liver, gallbladder, kidneys, and spleen and to increase the flow of bile. Combine the juices of carrot and cucumber with beetroot juice to cleanse the kidneys and gall bladder.

HOT FLUSHES

Eating beetroot is said to help decrease the severity and frequency of hot flushes in women going through menopause.

DECONGESTANT

Beetroot juice acts as a good decongestant if taken hot as soup or juice. The hot vapours help to clear catarrh, so maybe Gerard was right! A mix of beetroot, carrot and cucumber juices, lemon juice and a dollop of yoghurt is said to revive you after flu.

HEADACHE AND TOOTHACHE
The herbalists noted that beetroot vapours could clear the head. In Eastern Europe, where beetroot has been an important winter root crop since at least the fifteenth century, it is still used as a treatment for headache and toothache.

HAEMORRHOIDS
Beetroot is said to ease piles or haemorrhoids. A mix of beetroot and celery juice, mixed with live yoghurt and fresh mint leaves may do the trick; I'm assuming you drink this . . .

ACIDITY AND HEARTBURN
When stomach acid rises up towards the throat it is claimed that beetroot gives a soothing effect. Its effects on digestion may relieve other problems associated with the stagnation of food, such as skin problems and lethargy.

Growing Your
Own Beetroot

Growing beetroot isn't difficult, if you prepare the soil well beforehand. You can grow most varieties on any soil, so beetroots aren't fussy vegetables. I've usually steered clear of root vegetables in my garden because of the heavy clay soil, but my first experiments with beetroot proved a great success. The only trouble was, I didn't grow enough of them! Still, my experiments did wonders for the vegetable, in my opinion. It was my mother who suggested them, as she likes beetroot a lot and she lives with us. I have to admit she was right (again).

Growing beetroot doesn't have to mean you have a large vegetable plot in the garden. Several varieties are highly ornamental and can be grown in mixed beds, cottage style. This is also a good way of avoiding pests, which can attack whole rows of similar crops. You could try Cook's Delight, Bull's Blood, or the delightfully named MacGregor's Favourite, which makes me think of Beatrix Potter and Peter Rabbit.

PATIO PLANTERS
An ideal way to produce a few beets for early eating is to grow them in containers, or even in window boxes. The leaves will look pretty as they grow, and as you harvest the beets you will have space for other salad crops.

PREPARING THE GROUND
Beetroot prefers medium to light soil, although any well prepared soil will do, as long as it has not been recently manured, otherwise the roots are likely to grow into odd shapes. If you are into soil testing, a pH of 6.5 to 7.5 is the best. Use a plot which was well-prepared for a previous crop, such as beans, or brassicas. Soil dug in the autumn (if you can get on the ground and it's not too wet) and left for winter frost to break up is also good. When digging, remove as many stones as possible and all perennial weeds, like dandelions and docks, which will compete with the beetroot and may also harbour disease and pests. If you have room, rotate the crops you grow, as described in the next chapter.

SOWING THE SEED
Sow the seed when the danger of hard frost has passed.

This will depend on which part of the country you live in, but mid-April to May should be okay. If you want beetroot crops three or four weeks earlier, you can use a small poly-tunnel or cloches which should be put onto the ground to warm up the soil for a week or two. In this way you can sow the seed three or four weeks earlier than normal. If you want a succession of small plants, you should grow in small sowings until mid July. You can expect a yield of 12 round types or 6 long types per metre (yard).

Soaking the seeds in water for an hour or so before sowing will remove any chemicals present, but only soak enough seeds for one planting.

With a trowel or hoe, scoop out a line in the soil about 2.5 cm (1 in) deep. Leave a space of about 30 cm (1 ft) between lines or other crops. Water the soil before you place the seeds, about 5 cm (2 in) apart and then cover with soil. How long the seeds take to germinate will depend on the weather, but you should see signs of life in about 14 to 15 days. You may see a cluster of three or more seedlings growing together, or just one seedling. This will depend on the type of seed you used. Monogerm seeds will, as the name suggests, produce only one seedling, so they won't need thinning. If there are more, remove all but the strongest.

When the seedlings are about 5 cm (2 in) high, thin them to 10 cm (4 in) apart for round or globe varieties and 15 cm (6 in) apart for long varieties. If the weather gets very warm while the cloche or tunnel is still in place, take care that the seedlings don't get scorched. You may need to take the covers off during the day and just return them at night, and remember to water them if it doesn't rain.

If they are uncovered you might need to protect them from birds. The wood pigeons and collared doves can wreak havoc with our young crops, since the cat got too old to care, so we protect them with fine netting over old cloche frames. Another method is to cut the tops and bottoms off old, clear plastic drinks bottles, using them as collars. You could even use the bottoms of bottles as mini cloches, but I'm getting carried away now!

If conditions stay dry, water the plants to encourage quick growth and tender roots. Beetroot grows best near the sea (remember, it is derived from wild sea beet) and so one suggestion I've come across is to use a light application of common or rock salt around the plants when they are established. Don't let it get on the leaves. Since I live near the sea, I can't say I've tried this technique. It will of course deter slugs as well.

HARVEST GRADUALLY

The time before you harvest your beetroot will depend on the type, but will be somewhere between 9 weeks for common globe types and up to 18 weeks for long varieties. At 9 weeks the roots will be about 2.5 cm (1 in) in diameter and they will be at their most tender and ideal for salads or for eating raw. Pick your beets across the row to thin them out and encourage the rest to grow larger.

When the rest of the crop gets to about 8 cm (3 in) in diameter it is best to harvest them all and store them. If you leave them in the ground, they will become woody and lose flavour. If the leaves start to go limp that is a sign that the roots are ready for harvest.

STORAGE

If you don't want to eat the beets immediately, cut the leaves off about 5 cm (2 in) above the root. This will keep them fresh longer. Whatever you do, don't nick the roots, as they will bleed. Use a trowel to dig gently under the root, or gently pull it by the leaves. Store the beetroot in boxes, in layers and separated by sand or peat, in a cool dark place such as the garage or shed.

CONTAINER GROWN BEETROOT

Choose the largest container possible. A minimum size would be 30 cm (1 ft) in diameter. Fill the bottom with stones or old terracotta flower pot pieces, then cover with potting compost to about 5 cm (2 in) from the rim. Water well before you sow the seeds lightly over the surface and cover with a little more potting compost. As the seeds develop, thin them until there are about six plants for a 30 cm (1 ft) diameter pot, or more if the pot is larger. Just remember that pot grown plants need more water so don't let the pots dry out. Stand them in semi shade if possible.

PESTS AND DISEASES AFFECTING BEETROOT

Beetroot is relatively free from pests, apart from the birds, and most common varieties have been developed for their resistance to diseases. There are a few problems which you might need to look out for. The best ways to prevent them is to keep the area clear of weeds and debris.

MANGOLD FLIES (BEET LEAF MINER)
Maggots of this small fly tunnel into the leaves of spinach and beetroot. Leaves will have light brown blisters and may turn completely brown and fall off. Growth is stunted. You can spray in May for this, but I prefer to remove affected plants.

SWIFT MOTH
The caterpillars of this moth live in the soil and feed on roots of docks, nettles and beetroot. As this is a root problem, it may not be clearly seen at first. The plants look unhealthy and growth is stunted. There is no obvious leaf damage.
Remedy: good weed control is best to deter the caterpillars in the first place. Remove affected plants and destroy them.

RUST DISEASE
Slightly raised round spots (browny red) appear on the underside of the leaves.
Remedy: there is no real cure. You can spray with fungicide, but it is best to destroy affected foliage to prevent the spread.

APHIDS
Leaves curl and new shoots are distorted.
Remedy: remove aphids by hand, or encourage natural predators, such as blue tits. If you must, spray carefully to avoid harming beneficial creatures. Try a mild soap and water spray.

WHICH VARIETY?

With such a variety to choose from, I've tried to divide them into categories. A full list can be found at the back of the book. Most of the beetroot grown today has globe roots, although the first varieties which were cultivated had longer, tapering roots. These are still quite common in France, where, I have to admit, I didn't recognise the Rouge Crapoudine as a beetroot at all, on account of its ugly, rough skin and huge tapered root. Boltardy and Detroit are both globe varieties which are easy to cultivate and to buy seed for. Boltardy, as the name suggests, has built in resistance to bolting and was first introduced in the 1960s. It is used as a yardstick against which other beetroot are measured. Cheltenham Green Top and Long Red have cylindrical roots but there are also half-long varieties and flatter shapes, such as Crosby's Egyptian. A number of very old varieties, often known as heirloom or heritage varieties are still available from specialists, although these might not be so readily available or such an attractive proposition to start with. Breeding has made for a variety of textures and roots which may have discernable rings or zones. Modern processing techniques have made regular shaped roots popular for slicing, such as Cylindra and Forono. The current trend of buying mini beets, about the size of a large marble has also had an effect on varieties grown. Some are specifically grown with pickling in mind.

GEOSMIN AND FLAVOUR
If you don't particularly like the earthy taste of beetroot, then you can choose a variety which is low in this compound. Levels of geosmin vary between cultivars. Detroit Dark Red, a commercial variety from the USA, has the lowest concentrations and Chioggia (the pink and white one) has the highest. Some say that Chioggia, a heritage variety which has been around a lot longer, is bland, however, so the choice is up to you.

F1 HYBRIDS
Modern hybrids have improved growth and resistance to bolting as well as resistance to disease. Hybrids will not breed true, so you need to buy new seed every year

instead of saving some seed at the end of the season. Most hybrids are globe-shaped and have a good flavour.

MULTIGERM SEED
As stated earlier, beetroot seeds normally produce three or four seedlings, which need to be thinned quickly on germination. Most cultivars have multigerm seeds.

MONOGERM SEED
These are modern varieties which have been bred to produce only one seedling per seed. For the busy, part time gardener, they mean less thinning is required.

HERITAGE OR HEIRLOOM VARIETIES
These are the older cultivars, which have been around for more than 50 years. An example is Detroit Globe introduced in 1892. Detroit Globe was bred down from a variety described as an early maturing European Blood Turnip. Heritage varieties are not necessarily those chosen by commercial outlets, but those which people have been growing in the back garden or on the allotment for generations. If they didn't produce tasty beetroot, they wouldn't have been successful for so long, so they get my vote every time.

EARLY GLOBE VARIETIES

NAME	APPEARANCE	NOTES
Alvro Mono	Fine hairy roots.	Monogerm.
Avon early	Medium sized roots, organic.	Heritage variety. Good resistance to bolting.
Bikores	Well-developed tops, smooth-skinned dark red roots.	Dutch. Suitable for early sowing under cloches. Resistant to bolting, grows quickly, and stores well.
Centurion	Well-developed tops and blood-red flesh.	Roots do not bleed as much as other red beetroot.
Detroit Lora	Deep red.	High yielding.

Early Bunch	deep red flesh.	Very good bolting resistance, less successful as a main crop.
Early Wonder	Organic, smooth texture.	Sow March to May.
Libero	Smooth skinned, crimson.	Dutch, with good resistance to bolting.
Modena	Dark red colour.	Monogerm, good resistance to bolting.
Moneta	Smooth, uniform with good colour.	Monogerm, good resistance to bolting.
Monogram	Smooth, slightly flattened, deep red.	Monogerm, good resistance to bolting and can be sown early. It has smooth skinned globe-shaped roots, which are slightly flattened and deep-red in colour.
Pronto	Dark red.	Harvest when golf-ball sized. Ideal for pickling.
Red Ace	Smooth, intense red flesh.	Roots keep condition well. Ideal for showing.
Red Velvet	Green tops and smooth dark purple roots.	USA. Similar to Red Ace, has resistance to powdery mildew.
Solo	Green glossy leaves, dark-red roots.	Monogerm, F1 hybrid. Resistant to fungal diseases.
Smooth Crosby	Tall, smooth leaves and small roots.	Heritage, USA variety.

MAIN CROP GLOBE VARIETIES

NAME	APPEARANCE	NOTES
Action	Dark red flesh.	F1 hybrid, good resistance to bolting and disease. Multi-purpose beetroot.
Avenger	Flattened globe shape, tall glossy tops.	F1 hybrid, USA. Bred for sale as fresh greens and beetroot.

Big Red	Bright green leaves and dark roots.	F1 hybrid, USA. High sugar content.
Bluto	Large beetroot, deep red flesh with a fine texture.	Good storage properties.
Bolivar	Well-developed tops and uniform smooth-skinned roots.	Resistant to bolting, good for late season cropping. Grown commercially.
Boltardy	Smooth, deep red medium-sized, evenly-shaped roots.	Good texture, fresh sweet flavour. Often exhibited, grows well in containers.
Bonel	Upright foliage makes thinning and picking easier. Smooth deep-red flesh.	Good resistance to bolting, relatively high yielding and crops over a long period.
Boro	Smooth skins and dark roots.	Organically sourced, good storage performance. Suitable for both baby and standard production.
Bull's Blood	Dark crimson, broad leaves, almost black. Dark red roots with visible rings.	Heirloom pre 1900, ornamental. Can become tough with age. Leaves sweet when cooked.
Cardenal	Tops 30 cm (12 in) tall, smooth skinned, dark red flesh.	Roots lack fibre or zoning.
Chariot	Upright foliage for bunching and uniform, blood red roots.	F1 hybrid.
Covent Garden	Globe-rooted.	English heritage variety.
Crimson King	Medium to large roots.	Derived from Detroit varieties.

Crosby's Green Top	Well-developed green tops.	Bred from Crosby's Egyptian, introduced in 1951 from USA. Thrives under adverse conditions.
Darko	Bright-red flesh.	Bred by the French, good resistance to bolting.
Derwent Globe	Dark-red.	Developed in Tasmania, 1920s. Grown by gardeners in Australia.
Detroit Crimson Globe	Rich maroon colouring.	Popular improved Detroit, recommended for succession sowings.
Detroit Dark Red	Short, thick tops can be eaten when young.	Mature roots store very well. Popular with exhibition growers and recommended for containers.
Detroit Globe	Short tops and dark-crimson roots, good texture.	Heirloom, recently introduced to UK.
Detroit Rubidus	Firm smooth skin and deep red fibreless flesh.	Recent F1 hybrid, virtually no bolting.
Detroit Supreme	Medium-sized, smooth skinned, dark red roots.	No visible internal zoning, tolerant to fungal diseases.
Garnet	Smooth-skinned, very dark red flesh and little zoning.	USA 1964, similar to Detroit Dark Red.
Gladiator	Similar to Ruby Queen.	Introduced from USA.
Green Top Bunching	Flattened dark red globe, leaves good to eat and roots hold colour well.	Heirloom, USA, around 1940. Resistant to powdery mildew.
Ivax	Upright foliage with red flesh.	Monogerm.
July Globe	Red globe.	Heritage variety, dating from 1930s, rare today.
Kestrel	Bright green foliage with dark-red flesh.	F1 hybrid, USA, tolerant to a range of fungal diseases. Has a high sugar content.

King Red	Short tops, round roots and smooth crowns.	Introduced from USA in 1952. Adapted to peaty soils and high nitrogen content.
Kugel	Roots deep red colour.	Detroit-derived, stores well.
Modella	Red globe.	Monogerm, good bolting resistance.
Monopoly	Red flesh.	Newish monogerm with good bolting resistance.
Mono King	Medium top growth and small crown.	Monogerm, bred 1971.
Nobol	Related to Boltardy.	French cultivar, resistant to bolting.
Pablo	Smooth-skinned, dark-red flesh, no rings or zoning.	F1 hybrid, resistant to bolting. Roots mature and store without becoming woody, favoured for exhibition.
Preco	Well-developed tops, deep red flesh.	Bred in France.
Red Arrow	Upright leaves and roots with dark rings.	F1 hybrid.
Red Dart	Upright short top, small roots with very dark-red flesh.	Introduced 1979, only grown in USA.
Redpack	Globe cultivar.	Bred for processing in USA since 1965.
Regala	Small roots even when mature, purple/red.	Resistant to bolting and grows well in containers.
Rosette	Dark green leaf.	F1 hybrid.
Royal Delight	Uniform roots with deep red flesh and little zoning.	USA, introduced in 1982.
Royal Red	Medium-sized roots, smooth-skinned, dark-red.	Bred in 1962. Globe shape is flattened at the base.

Ruby Queen	Short green/maroon leaves. Roots bright red with shoulders.	Heritage, USA, 1950s. Sweet, buttery texture, performs well in poor soils.
Sangria	Tall green leaves, smooth purple roots.	Introduced from USA in 1980s.
Seneca Detroit	Tall tops, intense red, uniform root, low in fibre.	Heritage, USA from 1951, resistant to boron deficiencies.
Soloist	Deep red.	Monogerm, sweet flavour and high yields.
Ukrainian	Larger, staple crop beetroot.	Now only available as heritage variety from specialists.
Warrior	Fast-growing smooth round roots.	F1 hybrid from 1979. popular commercial beet for processing in USA.
Wodan	Bright red roots.	New F1 hybrid, doesn't go woody, good all rounder.

CYLINDRICAL, LONG ROOTED OR CONICAL BEETROOTS

NAME	APPEARANCE	NOTES
Bassano	Cylindrical, half long.	Heirloom Italian variety, ideal for producing uniform slices. Used as processing beet within the food industry.
Burpee Red	Flattened globe, uniform roots, dark-red in colour.	Introduced in 1953, selected from Crosby's Egyptian.
Carillon	Cylindrical, long-rooted with dark red flesh.	Good resistance to bolting and can be sown early. Good for slicing.

Cheltenham Green Top	Popular, large, long-rooted, deep purple with conical crown, skin rough and flesh slightly coarse.	Heritage variety, pre 1880s in England. Lower germination rate than most beetroot. Excellent flavour.
Cheltenham Monogerm	Long-rooted.	Monogerm, resistant to boiling.
Chicago Red	Long-rooted cultivar with purple flesh.	Particularly sweet.
Cook's Delight	Cylindrical (half-long) tankard shape. Dark red leaves.	Ornamental heritage, roots best when picked small and eaten young.
Crosby's Egyptian	Flattened heart shape. Glossy, green tops form abundant leaves.	Heirloom, from c1880 or earlier. Rapid early season growth and a resistance to bolting.
Cylindra (Butter Slicer)	Cylindrical, half-long or stump-rooted. Carrot like roots, dark purple and tender.	Danish variety; widely grown by 1880. Sweet flavour, ideal for cutting into uniform slices. Matures slowly but can be closely planted to give high yields. Tolerant of mildew, stores well.
Cyndor	Mid-green foliage, and dark red blunt-cylinder roots.	Resistant to bolting and curved root.
Early Blood	Turnip-shaped, dark red, with pink patches.	Heritage variety from USA, dating back to at least 1825. Sweet flavour.
Early Wonder	Large thick roots with slightly flattened globe shape. Dark-green and red leaves.	Probably first introduced in the 17th century. Less highly coloured than Egyptian.
Early Wonder Staysgreen	Tops stay green longer during cool weather.	From a selected line of Early Wonder.

Egyptian	Variable shape. Often deep red hearts, quick growing and early maturing.	Heritage variety, from 1870, resistant to bolting. Recommended for shallow soils and cold frames.
Feuer Kugel	Long rooted, smooth skinned.	From Switzerland. Stays tender and sweet to maturity, quite rare.
Formanover	Half long cylindrical with dark red sweet flesh.	Introduced from Denmark in 1963, excellent for processing, can be cropped late in season.
Forono	Long tankard shape, dark red with shoulders that can push above ground.	Good earthy flavour and yield, producing uniform slices. Stores well, good for pickling, but susceptible to bolting.
Long Blood Red	Long, deeply-buried root.	Heirloom from USA, 1885. Root is prone to forking. Rare.
Lutz Green Leaf	Half long purple globe, light green and pink leaves.	Heirloom variety, can grow large but retains good sweetness and texture.
MacGregor's Favourite	Long tapering roots with rounded shoulders. Good texture.	Ornamental, Scottish heirloom variety. Unusual spear-shaped leaves, shiny red, excellent to eat.
Mammoth Long	Long rooted, smooth skin, very dark red.	Sweet flavour.
Red Russian	Long-rooted cultivar.	From USA. The purple-red flesh is particularly sweet.
Rocket	Long-rooted smooth-skinned and red fleshed.	Now relatively rare.
Rouge Crapoudine	Almost black pock-marked and rough skin, broken by cracks and crevices, long irregular roots. Flesh is red, firm and sweet.	Heritage variety, one of the oldest known beetroot varieties, popular in France. It crops late in the season and can be sown to harvest in winter in areas with a milder climate, such as southern France.

| Sweetheart | Heart-shaped globe. | USA cultivar, by crossing a sugar beet with Detroit Dark Red. Large roots are as sweet as sugar beet. Introduced in late 1940s in USA. |
| Tall Top Early | Flattened globe with purple-red flesh. | USA variety. |

ALTERNATIVE COLOURED BEETROOTS

NAME	APPEARANCE	NOTES
Albina Vereduna	Smooth, thick skin, and pure white flesh. Leaves curled and wavy, and good for eating.	Dutch variety that has a particularly sweet and delicate flavour, sweeter than red beetroot, with potato like texture. Does not stain like red beetroot. Stores well but is prone to bolting.
Blankoma white	Slightly conical, with white flesh and thick skin. Good leaves for eating.	Heirloom Dutch variety, very sweet flavour. Blankoma is a globe heirloom. Dutch with ice-white flesh. The roots are round or slightly conical, thick skin, very sweet flavour. The leaves make good eating when cooked.
Burpee White	Globe with rat tail green tops and white-fleshed roots.	Introduced from USA, 1952. Sweeter than red beetroot.
Burpees Golden	Globe shaped orange/yellow roots. Leaves green.	Heritage, from Victorian times. Does not bleed and stain like normal beetroot. Tender, sweet tasting and fine texture.

Chioggia (Bulls eye or candy striped beet)	Slightly flattened shape, orange-pink outer skin, with a distinctive striped pattern of white and pink.	Heirloom Italian variety, described by 1840s. Pattern fades to pink when cooked, but is good for salad. Attractive green and red leaves have a mild flavour when raw or cooked.
Devoy	Long, dark pink flesh, red leaves.	Heritage, tender even when large. Stores well. Also in white.
Dobbie's Purple	Long tapering purple roots and leaves.	Heritage, from early 1900s. Can grow very large.
Doree	Golden-fleshed globe, smooth texture.	Very sweet flavour, good for pickling.
Eastern Wonder	Flattened globe.	USA, from 1953, adapted to sandy loam soils.
Snow White	Globe variety with pale white flesh.	Distinctive curly, waxy leaves.
Yellow Intermediate Mangel	A mangel, also eaten as a beetroot. Tapering orange-yellow skinned, whitish root.	Heirloom French, 1885. Roots grow large without loss of sweet flavour. Leaves can be steamed like chard. Keeps well.

MINI BEET VARIETIES

NAME	APPEARANCE	NOTES
Citation	Bright-green tops, small, very smooth, round roots.	From USA, cited for shipping over distance.
Detroit Tardel	Outstanding for root uniformity.	Well shaped and tender, ideal variety for baby beetroot, canning or pickling.
Detroit Little Ball	Smooth-skinned, dark red flesh, with distinct pale rings.	Ideal for pickling, fast-growing, resistant to bolting, and good for late sowing and storing.
Dwergina	Small globe, deep red flesh.	Good for pickling.
Monaco	Globe shaped.	Harvested young.
Moulin Rouge	Smooth-skinned and deep colouring.	A superb monogerm.
Pronto	Smooth-skinned with red flesh.	Recently introduced. Roots harvested when golf ball size, but can grow large. Good steamed whole, or pickled.
Red Ball	Tender greens and small dark roots.	Globe cultivar, specially for mini beets.

Growing Perpetual Spinach and Chard

Leaf beets will grow in ordinary garden soil but, like beetroots, prefer a pH above 6. You can plant them in rows or beds like you would spinach but, equally, you could use some of the beautifully coloured varieties as ornamentals, in a mixed bed with flowers. Leaf beets are not prone to bolting like ordinary spinach and can tolerate a wide range of weather conditions. Individual plants of some varieties can become quite large, but crowded plants will still produce well. The benefit of growing your own perpetual spinach is that you can harvest leaf by leaf, well into autumn and mild winters.

PERPETUAL SPINACH OR CHARD?

Leaf beet refers to all the varieties of perpetual spinach, spinach beet, chard and Swiss chard. They are all varieties of *Beta vulgaris*, which have been developed for their leaves rather than for swollen roots. The different names seem to have become interchangeable, although spinach beet seems to be called chard in the USA. The main difference seems to be in the size of plant and the stem length. Some of the chards look more like rhubarb stalks to me, and the variety of colour combinations available is greater with chard than with spinach beet. Cultivation is similar, so I'll refer to them all as leaf beets.

Chards can grow up to 60 cm (2 ft) in height and come in a range of colours. Most have green, shiny, ribbed leaves with stems or stalks in yellow, white and red. Chard has a slightly bitter taste and is usually served cooked like spinach, or in salads when young and tender. The main difference between chard and spinach is that chard leaves don't wilt to virtually nothing when cooked. The stalks can be stripped from the leaves and treated separately, liked asparagus. Leaves and stalks are both a good source of nutrients, including Vitamins A, B and C. Cultivars of chard include green forms, such as Lucullus and Fordhook Giant, and, as the names suggest, red-ribbed forms such as Ruby Chard, and Rhubarb Chard.

LEAF BEETS

These leaves are much smaller and tend to be smoother, with less stalk than chards. They are ideal for growing as a readily available spinach, which you can pick every day in season. Varieties include Erbette and Perpetual Spinach.

PREPARING THE WAY
The soil should be prepared in the same way as for beetroot, ie, digging in autumn if possible and clearing stones and perennial weeds out of the way.

For a simple way of rotating the crops, if you have room, divide your plot into three areas and plant, thus:

AREA 1
Group A
Choose from beetroot, carrots, celeriac, courgettes, aliums (onions), potatoes, peppers, pumpkins or tomatoes.

AREA 2
Group B
All types of beans, peas, spinach and lettuce. Beans and peas help fix nitrogen in the soil, so as well as providing a good crop of healthy vegetables, you'll improve the soil for future years.

AREA 3
Group C
Cabbage, broccoli, sprouts, cauliflower, swede, kale, kohl rabi, radishes.

Rotate planting in the groups as follows:

	Area 1	Year one	Year one
Year One	Group A	Group B	Group C
Year Two	Group B	Group C	Group A
Year Three	Group C	Group C	Group B

Over the course of three years, you can then give your vegetables what they want, as well as giving the soil a chance to improve. Of course, growing in beds with flowers means you don't really have the same problem, and you can just grow the plants where you have space or want the foliage to look good.

SOWING

The seed can be sown directly into watered soil, between April and July. Frost shouldn't be a problem. One planting should last all year, so make sure you site the plants well. Use a trowel or hoe to make a shallow drill. Plant the seeds about 2.5 cm (1 in) deep and about 5 cm (2 in) apart and then cover with soil. Leave a space of about 40 cm (15 in) between lines or other crops. As the seedlings grow, thin to about 20 cm (9 in), then thin again so that the plants are about 30 cm (12 in apart) You can eat these thinnings as salad leaves.

WATCH THE BIRDIES

Keep well watered and protect from birds, as for beetroot. If you want to grow chards for decoration in your vegetable plot, mix the seeds of two or more types before planting for an interesting and colourful effect.

HARVESTING

The beauty of spinach leaf beets is that you don't have to wait for ever for the plants to start producing. You should be able to start munching in 4 to 6 weeks. When harvesting, always pick from the outside of the plant so that you don't pick off the growing tip.

Chard can be harvested while the leaves are young and tender. If you want to eat the stems, wait for the plants to mature, when they will have slightly tougher stems. To avoid bitterness in hot weather make sure the plants get plenty of water.

If the plants get out of hand, cut off the larger, outer leaves and compost them. The inner leaves will quickly take their place.

PESTS AND DISEASES

Insect infestations are not usually a problem. Discard any affected leaves and don't compost them. Chard is resistant to most plant diseases. See the previous chapter for possible problems.

WHICH VARIETY?

Name	Description	Notes
Bright Lights	Stems or leaf mid-ribs in white, pink, red, purple, orange, yellow. Leaf blades green or bronzed, and crinkled.	Recently introduced, ornamental. Flavour milder than other chards. Leaves and leaf ribs can be cooked together or separately. Colourful mid-ribs make it a popular decorative addition to the vegetable garden.
Bright Yellow	Dark green leaves and distinctive yellow stems and veins.	Ornamental. Young leaves can be picked like perpetual spinch and will grow back.
Charlotte	Red leaf mid-ribs, green leaf blades.	Resists bolting better than others, more productive and has broader stems that are more cosistently coloured.
Chilean	Chard	Collection of colours, primarily ornamental.
Discovery	Upright, uniform plants have striking contrast of dark red against dark green.	F1 Hybrid, can be harvested early at 26—28 days. Exceptionally tolerant of cold.
Erbette	Type of spinich beet.	From Italy, can be continually cut throughout the growing season for greens. Good taste and texture.
Fordhook Giant	Thick white leaf stems, with large, glossy, crinkly, green leaves.	British Swiss Chard, heritage variety, introduced in 1934. It is high yielding and can supply greens throughout a growing season.
Large White	Large, glossy leaves with white mid-ribs.	Productive but not so tender. Less likely to bolt than red varieties, but more prone to pests.
Lucullus	White stalks and heavily crinkled leaf blades. Tall, hardy and prolific.	One of the oldest Chard varieties. Resistant to bolting. If left as a biennial, flower stalks can be eaten.
Monstruoso	White stemmed with broad, tender stalks.	Good overall quality.

Perpetual	Large, smooth, dark-green leaf blades, small leaf mid-ribs.	Heritage variety, introduced in Europe in 1869. Young leaves can be picked and the plant will regrow them. Highly prolific and resistant to bolting, can be continuously harvested all year round. Good resistance to drought.
Rainbow Chard or Five coloured Silverbeet	Leaf stems orange, yellow, pink, red, and white.	Ornamental heritage strain, dating back to Victorian Britain. However, the leaves are good to eat. Colourful in the border.
Rhubarb or Ruby Chard	Deep crimson leaf stems and veins with glossy, dark green and crumpled leaves.	Heritage chard variety, first introduced in the USA in 1857. Ornamental, but edible, ideal for flower beds or vegetable plot. Prone to bolting.
Ruby Red	Dark green, or reddish green, crinkly leaves and veins, red stems.	Improved Swiss Chard. Leaves and stems quite sweet.
Swiss Chard or Seakale Beet	Leaf beet with glossy dark green leaves, thickened stems and colourful leaf mid-ribs.	Known since ancient times. Can grow to 45 cm (18 in).
Vulcan	Red stems and dark green leaves.	A Swiss Chard cultivar with sweet-tasting leaves.

Cooking With Beetroot

Since becoming a beetroot fan I seem to find new ways of using it in dishes everywhere I look. Long gone are the days of cold, sliced beetroot in salad, with or without strong vinegar. Because beetroot has become so much more popular and the nutritional benefits have come to the forefront in the media, there are recipes galore. Here are some interesting ideas that I've come across. I've grouped them under various headings for convenience:

- **RAW BEETROOT**
- **SNACKS**
- **SALADS AND STARTERS**
- **SOUPS**
- **BEETROOT IN THE MAIN COURSE**
- **PICKLES AND CHUTNEYS**
- **OTHER RECIPES WHICH DEFY CATEGORY**

HINTS AND TIPS

PREPARATION

- If you are grating beetroot, or when peeling and slicing, use plastic disposable gloves or a clean plastic bag to hold the beet. That way you avoid pink fingers.
- If this advice is too late, the pigment is water based, so will wash out fairly soon.
- To remove beetroot stain from skin, rub with lemon juice and salt before washing with soap and water.

To avoid damaging the beetroot, it is better to cook before peeling it. Another useful precaution to preserve flavour and colour is to leave a few cm or an inch of the top (leaves) on while cooking. Once they bleed, they lose their rich colour, so don't be tempted to prick them to see if they are done. Although normally boiled, in France you can buy beetroot which have been cooked in ashes or charcoal, to give them extra flavour.

TO BOIL

Put beetroot in a pan of water, bring to the boil and cook for 40–45 minutes (less for smaller or baby beets). You don't need to add salt. There is plenty of sodium in beetroot.

TO BAKE
Preheat the oven to 170°C (325°F, Gas mark 3). Put the whole beets into a baking dish, cover with foil and cook for 1–2 hours. Exactly how long will depend on the size of the beets, type of oven and other cooking going on at the same time.

TO REMOVE SKINS
Wait until the beets have cooled down enough to handle. Rub the skins and they should come off easily.

HERBS AND SPICES
Those that go well with beetroot are: bay leaves, thyme, citrus fruits, chives, garlic, pepper, horseradish and mustard. Allspice (the dried berry of pimento officinalis), also known as Jamaica pepper, is particularly good with beetroot. Allspice is not a true pepper or a capsicum but has a hint of clove, cinnamon and nutmeg.

Balsamic vinegar is a strongly flavoured vinegar with a great deal of character. Others to try are wine vinegars (red and white) or raspberry vinegar.

BEETROOT SEASON
Beetroot is in season from July until the end of winter. Until September, when the main beetroot crop is lifted, the thinnings are sold as baby beets, although there are many varieties now produced specifically for serving as mini-beets. (see page 87). This is also when the leaves are suitable for use in salads. Beetroot can be bought raw or ready cooked, although they will have more flavour when freshly cooked. They are tasty served hot as a vegetable for many meat dishes and can be easily incorporated into many salad dishes, either raw or boiled.

FRESH BEETROOT
Beetroot can be eaten raw. You just need to peel it and it's ready to use, but be prepared for red hands. An exciting recent development is the new range of the baby beets, infused with vinegar and natural flavours. I bought some the other day, infused with lime juice in a raspberry vinegar and honey dressing. Delicious!

Some other ways to use raw beetroot:
- grate it finely to add to other vegetables
- add to a cheese sandwich
- grate it, Australian style, onto a burger
- make an ultra quick relish

HEALTHY SNACKS

Beetroot Crostinis   98

Dip for Beetroot and Carrot   99

Beetroot and Cheese Toasties   99

Pitta Bread with Beetroot and Smoked Salmon   100

Beetroot Muffins   101

Beetroot Salsa   101

Toasted Beetroot and Brie Baguette   102

Beetroot and Cheese Sandwiches   102

BEETROOT CROSTINIS

These will make an impressive snack or more substantial nibbles to go with pre dinner drinks. Allow 3 or 4 per person. For convenience you could use baguette or ciabatta, but you can use any type of bread — preferably wholemeal — sliced thinly. If, like me, you prefer goat cheese, this could be substituted for the mozzarella.

You will need: Serves 4

4 slices wholemeal bread
1 clove garlic
50 ml (2 fl oz) olive oil
2 medium, cooked beetroots
150 g (5 oz) mozzarella, drained
1 teaspoon balsamic vinegar
6 fresh basil leaves
cherry tomatoes, halved

Method

1. Using a pastry cutter, cut out 16 discs, 4 cm (2 in) in diameter, from the wholemeal bread. Rub the garlic over the bread and brush over with olive oil.
2. Toast the bread on both sides and place on a wire rack to cool and keep crisp.
3. Thinly slice the beetroot and cheese and brush with balsamic vinegar.
4. To serve, put a disc of beetroot onto a piece of toast, followed by the cheese. Garnish with basil and cherry tomato. Drizzle over a little more oil if you wish.

DIP FOR BEETROOT AND CARROT

This makes a change from the usual pepper, celery and carrot hors d'oeuvres round a pot of hummous. If you like it spicy, add some chilli sauce.

You will need:

125 ml (4 fl oz) crème fraiche
125 ml (4 fl oz) low fat yoghurt
3 tbsp horseradish sauce
1 spring onion, finely chopped
1 or more packs mini beets
2 carrots

Method

1. Mix all the ingredients together in a bowl and leave to combine for at least half an hour.
2. Cut the carrots into sticks and serve with cocktail beetroots for dipping.

BEETROOT AND CHEESE TOASTIES

If you have a sandwich toaster you can easily adapt this (with extra bread) into toasted beetroot and cheese sandwiches. Yummy!

You will need: Serves 2

    2 slices wholemeal or granary bread
    2–3 cooked beetroot, thinly sliced
    black pepper
    50 g (2 oz) cheese, grated or sliced

Method

1. Preheat the grill and toast the bread on both sides.
2. Put the beetroot slices on the toast, season with pepper and top with cheese.
3. Return to the grill until the cheese is golden.

PITTA BREAD WITH BEETROOT AND SMOKED SALMON

Salmon and beetroot sounds a bit strange together, but it is delicious.

You will need: Serves 2

    2 pitta breads, sliced to make pockets
    2–3 cooked beetroot, diced or thinly sliced
    110 g (4 oz) smoked salmon, cut into strips
    110 g (4 oz) low fat cream cheese
    black pepper
    watercress or salad leaves
    juice of half a lime

Method

1. In a bowl, mix the beetroot, lime, salmon and cream cheese together. Season with pepper.
2. Put some watercress or salad leaves into each pitta. Fill with beetroot and salmon.

BEETROOT MUFFINS

Goat cheese tastes particularly good with beetroot.

You will need: **Serves 6**

    1 pack breakfast muffins (split)
    butter or margarine (optional)
    250 g (9 oz) cooked beetroot, sliced
    110 g (4 oz) goat cheese, sliced
    black pepper

Method
1. Preheat the grill and lightly toast the muffins, smooth side up.
2. Remove and butter the split sides. Lay the beetroot slices on top — about 4 per muffin. Cover with the goat cheese, season lightly and return to the grill.
3. Serve as soon as the cheese is bubbling.

BEETROOT SALSA

This is tangy and good as a dip or side dish.

You will need: **Serves 4—6**

    2 cloves garlic, finely chopped
    1 teaspoon chopped fresh ginger
    2 tablespoons olive oil
    ½ teaspoon sweet paprika
    2 tablespoons lime juice
    250 g (9 oz) cooked beetroot, finely diced
    1 red onion, finely chopped
    2 tbsp chopped parsley or coriander

Method
1. Put the garlic and ginger into a pan with olive oil and fry for 2 minutes.
2. Stir in the paprika and lime juice and then the beetroot.
3. Cook for 1—2 minutes until the beetroot has taken up all the liquid. Turn into a bowl and leave to cool.
4. Mix in the onion and herbs to serve.

TOASTED BEETROOT AND BRIE BAGUETTE

You will need: Serves 2—3

   1 small baguette (or ciabatta)
   2 small red onions
   4 tsp olive oil
   2 tsp balsamic vinegar
   1 large clove garlic, halved
   250 g (9 oz) cooked baby beetroot
   200 g (7 oz) brie, sliced thinly
   salad leaves to garnish
   black pepper

Method

1. Preheat the grill. Cut the bread into thick slices and grill until golden.
2. Rub over with the garlic and drizzle over a little olive oil, pepper and balsamic vinegar.
3. Slice the beetroot and layer on each slice of toast and arrange the brie on top of the beetroot.
4. Return to the grill until the cheese has melted. Serve at once with a few salad leaves.

BEETROOT AND CHEESE SANDWICHES

You will need: Serves 2

   1 tablespoon low fat mayonnaise
   1 tablespoon low fat plain yoghurt
   50 g (2 oz) grated cheese
   ½ small red onion, finely chopped
   chopped cucumber
   2 medium cooked beetroots
   4 slices bread
   salad leaves

Method

1. Mix the mayonnaise and yoghurt together in a bowl. Add the cheese, onion and cucumber.
2. Divide the mixture between two slices of bread. Add salad and beetroot slices and bread to complete the sandwiches.

SALADS AND STARTERS

Beetroot for Hors-d'Oeuvre or Salad   104

Beetroot in Salad Dressing   104

     Mustard Cream Dressing   104

     Classic French Dressing   105

Spiced Dressing   105

Beetroot Provencal   105

Baby Beets with Cream Cheese   106

Beetroot Salad 'Belle Helene'   107

Swedish Potato Salad   107

Warm Chicken Salad with Beetroot   108

Beetroot, Avocado and Goat Cheese Salad   109

Beetroot, Avocado and Orange Salad   109

Beetroot, Parma Ham & Mozzarella Salad   110

Beetroot and Celery Salad   111

Beetroot, Olive and Feta Salad   111

Beetroot, Apple and Cheese Salad   112

Beetroot, Orange & Chicory Salad   112

Beetroot and Smoked Mackerel Salad   113

BEETROOT FOR HORS-D'OEUVRE OR SALAD

This is a traditional French way of serving beetroot as a starter. You can either bake, steam or boil the beetroot in water. It is often chopped into small cubes and seasoned with salt and pepper, vinegar, olive oil and parsley or chervil. Chopped, cooked onion can also be added. The primary school children I took to France on several occasions reacted in different ways to beetroot served as a starter for school dinner, but it is a very common starter, which French children eat in large quantities. Admittedly, this version has a few added ingredients, such as wine and horseradish.

You will need:

    sliced cooked beetroot
    red wine
    peppercorns
    bay leaf
    1 tablespoon English mustard or
    2 tablespoons grated horseradish

Method
1. Put the beetroot into a dish with ⅓ its quantity of grated horseradish.
2. Heat enough red wine with peppercorns and a bay leaf to cover the beetroot.
3. Pour over the beetroot and leave to marinate overnight.

BEETROOT IN SALAD DRESSING

Use freshly cooked beetroots. Cut into thin slices and marinate while still warm.
Here are some suggestions for salad dressings:

MUSTARD CREAM DRESSING
You will need:

    thick cream
    English mustard
    lemon juice
    salt and pepper

Method
Shake all the ingredients together and serve.

CLASSIC FRENCH DRESSING
I always use a screw topped jar to make a quantity of dressing, which can be kept in the fridge and used at short notice, whenever needed.

You will need:
> use 3 parts olive oil to one part wine vinegar
> 1 teaspoon French mustard
> 1 clove of garlic
> 1 teaspoon caster sugar
> salt and pepper

Method
Shake all the ingredients together and serve.

SPICED DRESSING
You will need:
> 1 teaspoon dill or caraway seeds
> ½ teacup boiling water
> 2 tablespoons wine vinegar
> 1 teaspoon salt
> 1 dessertspoon sugar
> freshly ground black pepper

Method
1. Bruise and crush the seeds and pour over the boiling water. Leave for 30 minutes.
2. Strain and add the vinegar, salt and sugar. Spoon over the beetroot and add pepper. Leave for some time before serving.

BEETROOT PROVENCAL

You will need:
> 275 g (10 oz) beetroot, baked
> 2 medium baked onions
> 1 tablespoon anchovy essence
> 1 teaspoon English mustard
> 1 tablespoon vinegar

3 tablespoons olive oil
freshly ground pepper

Method

1. Cut the cooked beetroot into cubes.
2. Puree the onions with the anchovy essence and the other ingredients to form a dressing.
3. Mix the beetroot with the dressing and serve.

BABY BEETS WITH CREAM CHEESE

This is a nice mix of hot beetroot and herby cheese. You could use bought, ready made herb cheese or substitute other herbs if you don't like coriander. I love it!

You will need: Serves 4

250 g (9 oz) cooked mini beetroots in mild vinegar
1 tablespoon olive oil
black pepper
200 g (7 oz) low fat cream cheese
1 clove garlic, crushed
1 tablespoon chopped chives
1 tablespoon chopped coriander
balsamic vinegar
mixed leaf salad

Method

1. Preheat the oven to 180°C (350°F, Gas mark 4)
2. Cut the beets in half and brush with a little olive oil. Arrange on a baking tray and place in the oven for about 3—4 minutes.
3. Meanwhile make a dressing with the rest of the olive oil, pepper and balsamic vinegar. Stir the herbs and garlic into the cream cheese.
4. Arrange salad leaves on a plate. Place the hot beetroots in centre, pour over dressing and top with the cream cheese. Serve immediately.

BEETROOT SALAD 'BELLE HELENE'

This interesting recipe incorporates a vegetable much underused in England, namely celeriac, which we see on our market in France all the time. Here, the stall holders will happily cut a large root in half if you don't want to buy a whole one. Very obliging of them!

You will need:

    1 celeriac root
    1 medium sized cooked beetroot
    25 g (1 oz) walnut pieces
    4 tablespoons mayonnaise

Method

1. Peel and cut the celeriac into thin sticks. Cook briefly in boiling water until almost tender.
2. Peel and slice the beetroot, or use a cutter to make small shapes.
3. Mix 3 tablespoons of the mayonnaise with the celeriac and put into a serving dish. Dilute the other spoonful of mayonnaise with a tablespoon of boiling water.
4. Put the beetroot round the edge of the dish and sprinkle the walnuts over the top. Pour over the remaining thinned mayonnaise and serve.

SWEDISH POTATO SALAD

This is another old favourite, especially good for summer buffets or barbecues. Very colourful — well, pink anyway.

You will need: **Serves 6**

    125 g (4½ oz) cooked beetroot
    700 g (1½ lb) new potatoes
    1 tablespoon chopped dill
    1 pickled dill cucumber
    5 tablespoons low fat yoghurt
    1 teaspoon lemon juice
    pepper
    2 tablespoons French dressing (see page 105)

Method
1. Wash the potatoes but don't peel or scrape. Cook them in boiling water until tender.
2. Drain the potatoes, cut into small chunks if necessary and mix with the French dressing while still hot. Leave to cool.
3. Mix the yoghurt and lemon juice together and season with pepper.
4. Put the diced beetroot, potatoes and cucumber with the yoghurt in a salad bowl and mix well. Add the dill and serve.

WARM CHICKEN SALAD WITH BEETROOT

You will need for the marinade: Serves 4

grated zest of an orange
1 clove garlic, crushed
1 teaspoon clear honey
2 tablespoons olive oil
1 teaspoon chopped rosemary
freshly ground black pepper

You will need for the salad:
4 small chicken fillets, sliced
250 g (8 oz) cooked beetroot
1 small onion, thinly sliced
2 medium oranges and their juice
mixed salad leaves
4 tablespoons olive oil

Method
1. In a large bowl, mix together the zest, garlic, honey, rosemary, seasoning and olive oil.
2. Add the chicken breasts and coat in the marinade. Cover and leave for an hour.
3. Prepare the salad by peeling the oranges, dividing into segments and halving them. Save any juice for the dressing. Slice the beetroot and halve them as well. Combine these with the salad and onion.
4. Make a dressing with olive oil and orange juice and pour over the salad. Put on plates ready to serve.
5. Heat a griddle pan to a medium high heat. Cook the

chicken with any left over marinade for about 8—10 minutes, turning regularly.

6. Place on top of the salad and serve immediately.

BEETROOT, AVOCADO AND GOAT CHEESE SALAD

This recipe combines another super food - avocado - as well as delicious goat cheese. Use a screw top jar to make the dressing and then if you don't need it all it will keep in the fridge until you want it. If you can't run to Parma ham, use thinly sliced bacon and cook until crispy.

You will need: **Serves 4**

    2 teaspoons olive oil
    80 g (3 oz) Parma ham (or bacon)
    250 g (9 oz) baby beetroot in mild vinegar
    2 avocados, sliced
    2 tablespoons toasted pine nuts
    125 g (4½ oz) soft, crumbly goat cheese
    salad leaves

You will need for the dressing:

    4 tablespoons extra virgin olive oil
    2 tablespoons balsamic vinegar
    black pepper

Method
1. Put the oil in a large frying pan. Fry the ham until crisp. Drain on kitchen paper.
2. Make a dressing with the ingredients above. Halve the beets and place in a bowl with the avocado, salad and pine nuts. Toss with the dressing.
3. Break up the Parma ham into bite-sized pieces and add to the salad. Crumble over the goat cheese and serve.

BEETROOT, AVOCADO AND ORANGE SALAD

Three super foods in one go! You can use grapefruit for this recipe instead, although some people can't eat it because of medication. This looks beautiful and tastes brilliant.

You will need: Serves 4

2 oranges (or 1 grapefruit)
1 large avocado, diced
175g (6 oz) cooked baby beets, sliced
mixed salad leaves
1 tablespoon chopped dill

You will need for the dressing:

3 tbsp olive oil
grated zest and juice of 1 lime
grated zest and juice of 1 orange
freshly ground black pepper

Method

1. Make the dressing by combining the ingredients above. Add the beetroot and leave for an hour or two.
2. Prepare the oranges by removing the peel and pith, and slicing horizontally. Cut each slice in half. Place on a plate with the salad leaves and avocado.
3. Spoon over the beetroot and dressing to serve, garnished with dill.

BEETROOT, PARMA HAM & MOZZARELLA SALAD

If you can get hold of it, you might like to try one of the golden beets or chioggia for this recipe, so that the beetroot colour doesn't take over.

You will need: Serves 4

250 g (9 oz) cooked beetroot slices
75 g (3 oz) Parma Ham
150 g (5 oz) mozzarella cheese, drained
salad leaves
fresh basil

You will need for the dressing:

3 tablespoons olive oil
1 tablespoon white wine or raspberry vinegar
1 teaspoon clear honey
freshly ground black pepper

Method

1. Put some salad leaves onto each plate. Drain the mozzarella cheese and slice as thinly as possible. Arrange with beetroot slices on the plates and drizzle over the dressing.
2. Put the Parma ham on top and garnish with basil to serve.

BEETROOT AND CELERY SALAD

You will need: **Serves 4**

>   250 g (9 oz) cooked beetroot, sliced
>   1 celery heart, finely sliced

You will need for the dressing:

>   1½ teaspoons wholegrain mustard
>   1 teaspoon honey
>   juice and grated zest of ½ orange
>   3 tablespoons olive oil
>   salt and freshly ground black pepper

Method

1. Put all the dressing ingredients in a screw topped jar and shake to mix.
2. Put the beetroot and celery in a bowl and pour over the dressing to serve.

BEETROOT, OLIVE AND FETA SALAD

If the saltiness of olives and feta cheese is too much, try mozzarella instead.

You will need: **Serves 4**

>   6 cooked beetroot in mild vinegar, sliced
>   125 g (4½ oz) feta cheese, drained and chopped
>   10 black olives, stoned
>   3 tablespoons olive oil
>   freshly ground black pepper
>   mixed salad leaves, washed

Method

1. Arrange the salad in a large bowl and add the beetroot and cheese.
2. Drizzle over with the olive oil and season to taste.

BEETROOT, APPLE AND CHEESE SALAD

You can use a prepared beetroot of choice for this recipe. There are many to choose from, including chilli as well as the usual citrus or raspberry flavours.
Sweetfire Beetroot is dipped in a natural chilli marinade.

You will need: Serves 4

    250 g (9 oz) beetroot infused with chilli or lime
    200 g (7 oz) cheddar cheese
    3 crisp eating apples, cored
    100 ml (4 fl oz) olive oil
    salad leaves, washed

Method

1. Dice the beetroot, apple and cheese into a bowl and lightly mix with olive oil.
2. Arrange the salad leaves on 4 plates and place a portion of the mixture in the centre.

BEETROOT, ORANGE & CHICORY SALAD

You get a good contrast of slightly bitter chicory with sweet orange here. If you don't like chicory, use salad and celery.

You will need: Serves 4
    2 cooked beetroot
    2 heads of chicory
    2 oranges

You will need for the dressing:
    50 ml (2 fl oz) olive oil
    black pepper

Method

1. Grate the zest from the oranges and place in a bowl with the olive oil and pepper.
2. Peel the oranges and remove pith. Divide into segments and add to the oil, along with any juice which seeped out.
3. Arrange 3 leaves of chicory on each of 4 plates. Slice the rest of the chicory into small strips and place in the centres of the plates, then arrange slices of beetroot over them.
4. Put the orange and oil over the top to serve.

BEETROOT AND SMOKED MACKEREL SALAD

You will need: Serves 4

 200 g (7 oz) cooked beetroot, diced or sliced
 2 fillets smoked mackerel with skin removed
 250 g (9 oz) baby spinach or salad leaves, washed
 2 tablespoons mayonnaise
 2 tablespoons low fat yoghurt
 1 tablespoon horseradish sauce

Method

1. In a small bowl, mix the mayonnaise, yoghurt and horseradish sauce. Leave for at least 30 minutes for the flavours to mix.
2. Flake the mackerel and check for any bones.
3. Put the salad leaves in a bowl. Scatter on the beetroot and mackerel.
4. Pour over the dressing and mix lightly. Serve immediately.

SOUPS

Borscht 1 (Beetroot soup)   114

Piroshki   115

Clear Beetroot Soup   116

Borscht Soup 2   116

Beetroot Gazpacho   117

Quick Beetroot and Apple Soup   117

Beetroot and Cabbage Soup   118

BORSCHT 1 (BEETROOT SOUP)

This is a modern method of making this traditional
Eastern European dish. There are many recipes around,
some more complicated and traditional than others.

You will need:

> 25 g (1 oz) butter
> 2 shallots or small onions
> 1 tablespoon flour
> 2 pints chicken or beef stock
> 2 large cooked beetroot
> 1 small carton crème fraiche
> salt and pepper

Method
1. Melt the butter in a large pan, add the chopped onions
and soften, but do not brown. Stir in the flour and then
the stock.
2. Grate or finely chop the beetroot and add to the soup.
Simmer until well flavoured and coloured, but do not
overcook it as the colour will be spoiled.
3. Blend the soup or sieve it and return to the pan. Check
the seasoning and add the crème fraiche just before
serving. Serve with Piroshki (see opposite page).

PIROSHKI

These dumplings are like dough balls and are traditionally served with borscht or with clear beetroot soup. They can be deep fried or baked in the oven. The size is up to you, but I would suggest making larger versions for baking and smaller ones for frying.

You will need for the dough:
110 g (4 oz) flour
1 egg
25 g (1 oz) melted butter
5 g (¼ oz) fresh or dried yeast
1 tablespoon warm milk
½ teaspoon salt
½ teaspoon sugar

You will need for the filling:
3 tablespoons boiled rice
1 hard boiled egg
50 g (2 oz) mushrooms
1 shallot or a few spring onions
10 g (½ oz) butter
oil for frying

Method
1. Prepare the yeast by mixing with the warm milk and sugar.
2. Sift the flour and salt together. Beat in the eggs and the milk mixture. Beat well to form a soft dough. Work in the butter and then cover and leave aside to rise for about 40 minutes. Knock down and chill in the fridge until you are ready to use it.
3. Meanwhile slice the mushrooms and cook in butter with the onion. Mix these ingredients with the rest of the filling.
4. When you are ready to cook the piroshki, roll out the dough and cut into rounds. Place a little of the filling on each base and fold over to make a turnover and seal the edges well with a damp brush or fork. Brush with milk if baking and leave for 10 minutes. If frying, plunge them into hot oil until browned. If baking, use a moderate oven and cook for about 10—15 minutes.

CLEAR BEETROOT SOUP

You will need:

    1 litre (2 pints) strong beef stock
    225 g (8 oz) minced beef
    whites and shells of 2 eggs
    1 glass sherry
    1 large raw, grated beetroot
    1 teaspoon salt
    crème fraiche

Method

1. Put the stock into large pan with the beef, whipped egg whites, shells, salt and the grated beetroot. Bring to the boil and simmer for 20—30 minutes.

2. Allow to cool slightly then strain through a fine sieve or cloth.

3. Just before serving, reheat, adjust seasoning and add the sherry. Serve with crème fraiche in a separate bowl and piroshki.

BORSCHT SOUP 2

This is a quick version of the famous Russian soup. It is delicious served with a swirl of sour cream or yoghurt. A food processor will cut down a lot of the preparation.

You will need: **Serves 6**

    450 g (1 lb) cooked beetroot
    2 carrots, shredded
    ½ head celeriac, finely chopped
    4 sticks celery, chopped
    1 small leek, sliced
    2 large potatoes, finely diced
    1.5l (3 pints) chicken or vegetable stock
    salt and freshly ground black pepper

To serve you will need:

    1 tablespoon chopped parsley
    crème fraiche or yoghurt

Method

1. Place all of the vegetables except the beetroot with the stock into a large saucepan and season well.
2. Bring to the boil, cover and simmer for 25 minutes.
3. Stir in the beetroot and cook for another 15 minutes.
4. Blend in a processor until smooth.
5. Serve with a swirl of crème fraiche and parsley.

BEETROOT GAZPACHO

This chilled summer classic is salt and garlic free.

You will need: **Serves 2—3**

    200 g (7 oz) cooked beetroot in malt vinegar
    400 g (14 oz) can tomatoes
    ½ cucumber
    ½ red pepper
    3 tablespoons olive oil
    chopped chives for garnish
       and a slice of cucumber per bowl

Method

1. Put all the ingredients into a blender until smooth.
2. Chill until required and serve garnished with chives and cucumber.

QUICK BEETROOT AND APPLE SOUP

Another chilled soup for hot weather.

You will need: **Serves 4**

    250 g (9 oz) cooked beetroot, chopped
    2 spring onions, chopped
    570 ml (1 pint) pure apple juice
    2 teaspoons lemon or lime juice
    125 ml (4 fl oz) low fat plain yoghurt

Method

1. Put all of the ingredients except the yoghurt into a blender until smooth.
2. Chill until required and serve with a swirl of yoghurt.

BEETROOT AND CABBAGE SOUP

You can use canned beetroot for this soup to save time. For a much better flavour however, use a food processor to grate beetroot and apple and shred the cabbage. Serve this soup hot or chilled.

You will need: Serves 4—6

> 4 medium beetroot, peeled and grated
> 250 g (9 oz) red cabbage
> 2 onions, chopped
> 1 large apple, peeled, cored and sliced
> 2 tablespoons olive oil
> 2 tablespoons tomato puree
> 125 ml (4 fl oz) white wine
> I litre (2 pints) chicken or vegetable stock
> 200 g (7 oz) low fat yoghurt
> chopped chives or parsley for garnish

Method
1. Heat the oil in a large pan. Add the onion and cook for 3—4 minutes.
2. Add the beetroot, apple, cabbage, stock and tomato puree and bring to the boil. Cover and simmer for 10 minutes.
3. Add the wine. If serving hot, do so at once. If serving cold, allow to cool and refrigerate for at least an hour.
4. Serve with a swirl of yoghurt and a garnish of herbs.

MAIN COURSE DISHES AND ACCOMPANIMENTS

Braised Red Cabbage and Beetroot 119

Baked Beetroot 120

Sweet and Sour Beetroot 121

Beetroot with Lemon and Cream 122

Spiced Beetroot and Apple Sauce for Roast Pork 122

Beetroot Tabbouleh 123

Pink Mashed Potatoes 123

Beetroot Salmon Parcels 124

Beetroot and Beef Casserole 124

Baked Courgettes, Beetroot and Mushrooms 125

Chicken and Beetroot Rolls 126

Baby Beets and Turnips with a

Goat Cheese Sauce 127

Beetroot and Mushroom Tartlets 127

BRAISED RED CABBAGE AND BEETROOT

This is becoming a firm family favourite, originally served at Christmas with hot or cold turkey. Now I cook it all winter to serve with sausages or any roast. The quantity made doesn't have to be a problem if you can't eat it all at once. The cabbage seems to improve with cooking and you can happily reheat the leftovers, or freeze some for another time.

The prunes are a delicious addition, but not to everyone's taste. This is a great way to slide them into the diet when nobody is looking, although I haven't had complaints, even when they are spotted!

You will need: Serves 6

450 g (1 lb) red cabbage
225 g (8 oz) onion, chopped
1 cooking apple, peeled, cored and chopped
2 medium beetroots, boiled peeled and chopped
75 g (3 oz) ready to eat prunes, halved
2 tablespoons orange juice
3 tablespoons wine vinegar
half a whole nutmeg
pepper

Method
1. Throw away the outer leaves of the cabbage and cut into quarters. Remove the stalk and shred the cabbage.
2. In a large casserole, put a layer of cabbage, followed by a layer of onion, prunes, apple and beetroot. Season well with nutmeg and pepper, then add another layer of cabbage.
3. Pour over the vinegar and orange juice and cover with a tight lid.
4. Cook slowly at 150°C (300°F, gas mark 2) for at least 2 hours.
5. Cool slightly before serving.

BAKED BEETROOT

This is a very simple but delicious way to eat beetroot. Now that crème fraiche can be bought with reduced fat, it is also a very healthy way to eat it. In France I use 15% fat, but you can even get 4% versions in some places. The microwave version is a good way to cook beetroot quickly, although you lose some of the colour and flavour by pricking them and they risk becoming rubbery.

You will need: Serves 4

4 raw beetroot, each approximately 225 g (8 oz)
crème fraiche
salt and pepper

Oven Method

1. Preheat the oven to 180°C (350°F, gas mark 4).
2. Wash the beetroot but do not peel. Wrap in foil and place in a greased ovenproof dish and bake for about 2 hours. If they are larger, give them longer. The skins will slide off when they are ready.
3. To serve, slice off the top of each beetroot and top with a spoonful of crème fraiche. Season to taste.

Microwave Method

1. Prick the beetroot skins with a fork. Arrange in a shallow dish with 3 tablespoons water.
2. Cook on High for 20–25 minutes, depending on the power of your microwave.
3. Serve as above.

SWEET AND SOUR BEETROOT

This quick and easy recipe goes well with roast beef or pork.

You will need:

    2 large cooked beetroots
    25 g (1 oz) butter
    1 teaspoon salt
    3 tablespoons vinegar
    2 tablespoons sugar
    freshly ground black pepper

Method

1. Peel and chop the beetroots.
2. Place in a pan with all the other ingredients and stir until thoroughly hot. Add more salt or pepper if necessary.
3. Serve hot.

BEETROOT WITH LEMON AND CREAM

This simple side dish will go well with any meat or fish dish.

You will need: Serves 4

    250 g (9 oz) cooked beetroot
    zest of a lemon, grated
    150 ml (5 fl oz) single cream
    freshly ground pepper
    2 tablespoons fresh breadcrumbs

Method
1. Preheat oven to 180°C (350°F, gas mark 4), and grease a shallow oven-proof dish.
2. Cut the beetroot into thick slices and arrange them in the dish, overlapping them slightly. Sprinkle over the lemon zest.
3. Pour on the cream and season with pepper.
4. Bake for 20 minutes before removing from the oven.
5. Cover with breadcrumbs and brown under a hot grill.

SPICED BEETROOT AND APPLE SAUCE FOR ROAST PORK

You will need:

    1 medium beetroot
    1 medium apple
    25 g (1 oz) butter
    2 tablespoons water
    ½ teaspoon cinnamon
    4 whole cloves

Method
1. Peel and grate the apple and the beetroot.
2. Melt the butter in a saucepan. Add the grated vegetables and a couple of tablespoons of water, plus the cinnamon cloves.
3. Simmer, stirring occasionally for a few minutes, until the beetroot is tender and the liquid has nearly all evaporated.

BEETROOT TABBOULEH

Serve this with grilled meat, chicken or fish.

You will need: **Serves 4—6**

    125 g (4½ oz) bulgar wheat
    250 g (9 oz) baby beetroot in mild vinegar, diced
    150 ml (5 fl oz) boiling water
    4 spring onions, chopped
    2 tomatoes
    chopped mint and parsley

You will need for the dressing:

    4 tablespoons olive oil
    1 tablespoon lemon juice
    black pepper

Method
1. Put the bulgar wheat into a bowl, pour over the boiling water and set aside to soak for 45—60 minutes, until the water has been absorbed.
2. Chop the tomatoes into small pieces and place in a large salad bowl, along with the beetroot, herbs and spring onions.
3. Mix in the wheat. Mix the dressing ingredients together and pour over the wheat. Stir to toss gently.

PINK MASHED POTATOES

You will need: **Serves: 4—6**

    250 g (9 oz) cooked beetroot, drained
    450 g (1 lb) good mashing potatoes, peeled and quartered
    knob of butter and dash of milk
    freshly ground black pepper

Method
1. Cook the potatoes in a large saucepan with plenty of water.
2. Drain when cooked and add the beetroot to the potatoes in the pan.
3. Mash together, adding butter and milk if you like. Season with pepper and serve hot.

BEETROOT SALMON PARCELS

Here's that combination of salmon and beetroot again. If you like the tangy taste of horseradish, you can add it to the parcels.

You will need: **Serves 4**

    1 tablespoon virgin olive oil
    4 salmon fillets
    250 g (9 oz) cooked beetroot, sliced
    4 tablespoons white wine
    Freshly ground black pepper
    4 teaspoons horseradish sauce (optional)

Method
1. Preheat the oven to 190°C (375°F, gas mark 5).
2. Prepare 4 squares of kitchen foil, making each large enough to loosely wrap a piece of salmon. Lightly oil each square and place a fillet in the middle, skin side down.
3. Put 2–3 beetroot slices on top with a teaspoon of horseradish (optional). Turn up the sides of the foil, and pour wine over each fillet. Season lightly and close the foil parcels so there is room inside for air to circulate.
4. Bake for about 20 minutes. Open the parcels carefully to avoid losing any liquid. Serve with new potatoes and broccoli.

BEETROOT AND BEEF CASSEROLE

The addition of beetroot to an orange and beef casserole makes a delicious combination.

You will need: **Serves 4**

    450 g (1 lb) lean casserole steak, trimmed and cubed
    2 tablespoons olive oil
    1 clove garlic, crushed
    250 g (9 oz) onions, sliced
    250 ml red wine or vegetable stock
    zest and juice of an orange
    salt and black pepper
    250 g (9 oz) cooked beetroot
    1 tin tomatoes, chopped

Method
1. Preheat the oven to 170°C (325°F, gas mark 3).
2. Heat half the oil in a flame proof casserole dish. Brown the beef and then remove the meat and set aside on a plate.
3. Add the onions and garlic to casserole and fry gently for 5 minutes, stirring occasionally.
4. Add the tomatoes, red wine or stock and orange. Stir together and season with salt and pepper.
5. Return the meat to the casserole and arrange slices of beetroot on top.
6. Cover and cook in the oven for 2 hours.

BAKED COURGETTES, BEETROOT AND MUSHROOMS

You will need: Serves 4

4 medium courgettes, sliced
1 medium onion, finely chopped
200 ml (7 fl oz) cream
1 vegetable stock cube
50 ml (2 fl oz) horseradish sauce
300 g (11 oz) cooked, diced beetroot
225 g (8 oz) mushrooms
25 g (1 oz) butter

Method
1. Preheat the oven to 160°C (325°F, gas mark 3).
2. Blanch the courgettes in boiling water for 2–3 minutes. Drain and arrange in an oven proof dish with the beetroot.
3. Melt a little butter in a saucepan, add the onion and mushroom and gently soften. Add the cream and warm before sprinkling in the stock cube and stirring until dissolved. Stir in the horseradish.
4. Pour the cream mixture over the beetroot and courgettes. Bake until the cream has set (approx 15 minutes).

CHICKEN AND BEETROOT ROLLS

If you can get it you could use a 250 g (9 oz) pack of beetroot infused with chilli for this recipe. If you don't like chilli, use ordinary beetroot or one of the infused varieties, eg lime.

You will need: Serves 4

    4 boneless chicken breasts
    200 g (7 oz) cooked beetroot
    1 clove garlic, crushed
    1 sweet chilli, chopped finely (optional)
    1 tablespoon balsamic vinegar
    1 tablespoon honey
    pepper

You will need for the dressing:
50 g (2 oz) baby beets infused with chilli
½ teaspoon balsamic vinegar
1 teaspoon olive oil

Method
1. Skin the chicken pieces and flatten them between sheets of cling film with a rolling pin until thin.
2. Place all the other ingredients in a processor and blend until smooth but thick.
3. Spread the beetroot paste over the chicken breasts, keeping away from the edges. Now roll them up into sausages, turning the ends in, and secure with cocktail sticks. (You could use clean muslin if available).
4. Bring a pan of water to the boil and poach the chicken rolls for 15–20 minutes. Remove and leave to cool. Chill until required.
5. To make the dressing, puree the beetroot with the oil and vinegar to a spooning consistency. You may need more oil if the mix is too stiff.
6. To serve, cut each chicken piece in half and pour over the dressing. Serve with a baby leaf salad and new potatoes.

BABY BEETS AND TURNIPS WITH A GOAT CHEESE SAUCE

Serves 4 as an accompaniment or 2 as a main course.

You will need:

8 miniature beets, uncooked, with leaves still attached
8 miniature turnips
125 g (4½ oz) goat cheese
bunch of fresh coriander leaves

Method

1. Carefully wash the beetroots and turnips to avoid breaking the skin. Chop the tops off the beetroot and wash separately.
2. Place beets and turnips in separate pans to boil until tender. Drain the turnips and remove the beets. Blanch the leaves in the beet water for a minute, until wilted.
3. Remove the skins from the beetroot and turnips. Arrange the vegetables and the leaves in a grill proof dish.
4. Heat the goat cheese gently in a saucepan and stir in the coriander. Pour over the vegetables and place under a preheated grill until bubbling. Serve immediately.

BEETROOT AND MUSHROOM TARTLETS

If you prefer to make a more substantial case, use ready made short crust pastry for these tasty tartlets.

You will need:

200 g (7 oz) filo pastry cut into 12 cm squares
1 medium onion, finely chopped
1 vegetable stock cube
200 ml (7 fl oz) cream
50 ml (2 fl oz) horseradish sauce
300 g (11 oz) cooked beetroot, diced
300 g (11 oz) mushrooms
50 g (2 oz) melted butter

Method

1. Preheat the oven to 130°C (250°F, gas mark ½).

2. Use an upturned dish as a mould to make the cases. Brush the bottom and side of the dish with butter and butter the sheets of filo pastry. Arrange 3 sheets over the mould to make each case.

3. Place on a baking tray and bake for 10—15 minutes or until the pastry is crisp and golden brown. Remove the tray and turn the oven up to 160°C (325°F, gas mark 3).

4. Meanwhile melt a little butter in a saucepan, add the onion and gently cook until soft. Add the cream and stock cube, stirring until dissolved. Add the horseradish.

5. Divide the beetroot between the 4 pastry cases and then pour on the cream mixture. Bake for about 15 minutes.

6. Sauté the mushrooms in butter and arrange in the centre of each tartlet. Serve with salad.

PICKLES AND CHUTNEYS

Spiced Vinegar   129

Pickled Beetroot   129

Pickled Beetroot 2   130

Piccalilli   130

Piccalilli 2   131

Ultra Quick Beetroot Relish   131

Beet Relish   132

Hot Beet Relish   132

Beetroot Chutney   133

Beetroot and Onion Chutney   133

SPICED VINEGAR

This is a basic vinegar for use in pickling.

You will need:

   575 ml (1 pint) vinegar
   25 g (1 oz) black peppercorns
   10 g (½ oz) root ginger
   10 g (½ oz) salt
   7 g (¼ oz) allspice
   10 g (½ oz) finely chopped shallots
   2 cloves garlic, crushed
   2 bay leaves

Method
1. Grind the peppercorns and mix together with all ingredients in a wide necked jar. Cover and allow to rest for a week.
2. Place the jar, opened, in a saucepan of boiling water and simmer for 1 hour. When cold, cover tightly and store, or use for pickling.

PICKLED BEETROOT

First, boil the beetroots in their skins. Don't trim anything as the colour will start to fade during cooking. Add a little vinegar to the water before boiling them. They don't need to be fully cooked. Remove from the water and let them cool.

Heat up enough vinegar to cover the beets, with a teaspoon of whole peppers and the same of allspice. Simmer for 15 minutes. Peel and cut the beets into slices and put them into clean jars. Cool the vinegar and pour over the beets. Cover the jars with waxed paper or non metallic lids.

PICKLED BEETROOT 2

You will need:

> beetroot
> spiced vinegar
> 1 teaspoon salt per jar
> allspice
> pepper

Method

1. Wash the beets but take care not to damage their skins. Wrap in foil and bake in a moderate oven 180°C (350°F, gas mark 4) for about an hour (more if they are very large).

2. Cool, peel and slice or cube the beetroot and sprinkle over the salt. Pack into jars and cover with cold spiced vinegar (see page 129). Cover and store in a cool place.

PICCALILLI 1

This is a Victorian recipe. Use the spiced vinegar recipe on page 129.

You will need a mixture of any of the following:

> cauliflower
> onions
> gherkins
> French beans
> green peppers
> beetroot

Method

1. Cut the vegetables into small chunks and cook in boiling, strongly salted water for 3 minutes. Cook the beetroot in its skin separately to avoid 'bleeding.'

2. Drain, cool and allow the vegetables to dry thoroughly on large plates.

3. Add a large pinch of turmeric and of curry powder to each pint of the spiced vinegar recipe. Take a tablespoon of mustard powder and mix with a little cold vinegar to make a paste. Add this to the spiced vinegar as it cools after the boiling period.

4. Combine all of the ingredients in jars and cover with vinegar. When cold, cover and store.

PICCALILLI 2

You will need:

    225 g (8 oz) cauliflower florets
    125 g (4½ oz) French beans
    125 g (4½ oz) raw beetroot, peeled
    225 g (8 oz) pickling onions
    225 g (8 oz) diced cucumber
    125 g (4½ oz) salt
    1 teaspoon turmeric
    3 teaspoons dry mustard
    ½ teaspoon ground ginger
    75 g (3 oz) sugar
    430 ml (¾ pint) malt vinegar
    4 teaspoons cornflour

Method

1. Put the vegetables, chopped and sliced, in a colander and add the salt. Leave to stand for as long as possible, then rinse and drain.
2. Mix the ginger, sugar, turmeric and mustard with a little of the vinegar. Add all but a few tablespoons of the remaining vinegar and put in a saucepan with the vegetables.
3. Simmer gently for about 5 minutes. Don't let the vegetables go soggy.
4. Mix the remaining vinegar with the cornflour, add to the pan with the vegetables and bring to the boil, stirring carefully.
5. After 3 minutes, spoon to mix into wide necked jars, cool and cover.

ULTRA QUICK BEETROOT RELISH

You will need:

    250 g (9 oz) medium cooked beetroot in mild malt vinegar, diced
    2 teaspoons horseradish sauce
    1 tablespoon chopped parsley

Method

1. Put the diced beetroot in a bowl and stir in the horseradish and parsley. Set aside until required.

BEET RELISH

You can use large, less tender beetroot for this relish which hails from the north of England. It is a good accompaniment to cooked meat and is even better if matured in a cool place for 2 or 3 months. A food processor would be handy for the shredding and grating.

You will need:

900 g (2 lb) cooked beetroot, skinned and cubed
450 g (1 lb) white cabbage, shredded
75 g (3 oz) fresh horseradish, grated
1 tablespoon English mustard powder
570 ml (1 pint) malt vinegar
225 g (8 oz) sugar
salt and pepper
pinch cayenne pepper

Method
1. Put all the ingredients into a large saucepan and bring slowly to the boil. Simmer and stir for half an hour.
2. Preheat some clean jars and pack the relish in, covering immediately with non metallic or vinegar proof tops.
3. Store to mature.

HOT BEET RELISH

You will need:

3 cups cold boiled beets, grated
½ cup horseradish
¾ cup vinegar
1 teaspoon salt
3 tablespoons caster sugar
pepper

Method
1. Boil, peel and grate the beets and add the horseradish.
2. Season with salt, pepper and sugar.
3. Add as much vinegar as will be absorbed by the beets and horseradish.
4. Store in covered jars. This keeps well.

BEETROOT CHUTNEY

You will need:

2½ lb cooked beetroot
225 g (8 oz) onions, skinned
225 g (8 oz) raisins, stoned
1 tablespoon salt
2 cloves
½ tablespoon allspice
4 black peppercorns
175 g (6 oz) sugar
¾ pint (15 fl oz) vinegar

Method
1. Peel and chop the beetroot.
2. Put the chopped onion in a saucepan with the raisins, salt, spices, sugar and vinegar. Bring to the boil and simmer gently until the mixture thickens and the onion is cooked.
3. Add the beetroot and continue to cook until blended with the other ingredients.
4. Cool, bottle and cover.

BEETROOT AND ONION CHUTNEY

This is a light, fresh tasting chutney that's really easy to make.

You will need:

110 g (4 oz) cooked beetroot in malt vinegar, drained and
chopped
150 g (5 oz) onions, chopped
150 g cooking apples, peeled and chopped
2 tablespoons demerara sugar
pinch of ground ginger
80 ml (3 fl oz) malt vinegar
1 teaspoon salt

Method
1. Mix all the ingredients together in a large saucepan. Bring to the boil and simmer gently, stirring occasionally, for 45 minutes.

2. Put into warmed, clean jars, while still hot and cover with jam lids or screw-on lids.

3. Store in a cool dark place until required.

OTHER RECIPES WHICH DEFY CATEGORY

All of the following are of interest rather than recommended eating or consumption.

17TH CENTURY SPICED BEETROOT SALAD

I've put this recipe in to show that beetroot has been around as a vegetable for a long time. I can't say I've tried it, but it is interesting to read. As you can see, spelling was not standardised back then.

From The English Hus-Wife, Gervase Markham, 1615

'Take a good quantity of blauncht Almonds and with your shredding knife cut them grosly: then take as many Raisyns, and the stones pickt out, as many figges shred like the Almonds, as many Capers, twice as many Olives, and as many currants as of all the rest, cleane washt; a good handful of the small tender leaves of red Sage and Spinage: mix all these well together with good store of Sugar, and lay them in the bottome of a great dish, then put unto them Vinegar and Oyle, and scrape some Sugar over all: then take Orenges and Lemons, and paring away the outer pills, cut them into their slices, then with those slices cover the sallat all over; which done, take the thinne leafe of the red Coleflowre, and with them cover the oranges and lemons all over, then over those red leaves lay another course of olives, and the slices of well pickled coucumbers, together with the very inward heart of your Cabbage Lettice, cut into slices, then adorne the sides of the dish and the top of the Sallat with mo slices of Lemons and Oranges, and so serve it up'

'To compound an excellent sallat and which indeede is usual at great feasts, and upon Princes tables.'

BEETROOT WINE

If you use fresh yeast for the fermentation, prepare it with a little lukewarm water before you start. If dried yeast is used, follow the instructions provided on the packet.

You will need:

5 lb beetroot

1 gallon water

3 lb sugar

¾ oz fresh yeast or 1 level teaspoon dried yeast

Method

1. Wash and peel the beetroot, taking care to remove all dirt. Cut them up and put in a large pan with the water and cook until tender.
2. Add the sugar and leave to stand for 24 hours.
3. Strain off the liquid and add the prepared yeast.
4. Pour into a jar with a fermentation lock on and allow to ferment at room temperature for about 3 weeks, or until all the bubbles have stopped forming. The time will depend on the rate of fermentation and the temperature.
5. Siphon off into a clean jar and cork firmly.
6. When all the sediment seems to have settled, after 5 or 6 weeks, rack off the wine and bottle.

CHOCOLATE BEETROOT CAKE

You will need: Serves 6—8

2 tablespoons cocoa powder

125 g (4 oz) plain flour

1.5 teaspoons baking powder

pinch of salt

150 g (5 oz) caster sugar

240 ml (8 fl oz) corn oil

1 teaspoon vanilla essence

3 whole eggs, beaten

200 g plain cooked beetroot (not with vinegar)

110 g (4 oz) plain dark chocolate, chopped into small pieces

Method

1. Preheat the oven to 190°C (375°F, gas mark 5). Grease and line an 18 cm (7 in) cake tin.
2. Sift the cocoa, flour, baking powder and salt into a large mixing bowl and mix in the sugar. Add the rest of the ingredients and mix well.
3. Pour the cake mix into the tin and bake for 50 minutes — until still sticky in the middle.
4. Turn out and cool on a rack. Serve with a helping of crème fraiche.

Spinach
Recipes

This section contains a lot of recipes for using perpetual spinach and chard. The flavour of leaf beet spinach and ordinary spinach is almost the same, so you can substitute one for the other. Chard leaves can also be eaten as spinach, but will need longer in cooking. The leaf stems of chard can be treated like asparagus and are therefore cooked separately.

Even if you can't get hold of the more exotic varieties of chard, most of the recipes will work with any kind of *Beta vulgaris* leaves as well as ordinary spinach.

PREPARING SPINACH OR CHARD
First trim the bottom end of the stalks. If you find chard stalks are very fibrous, peel away some of the fibres, like you would do with celery.

Wash well to remove any sand or soil that may be hidden in the leaves. The best way to do this is to immerse the leaves in a large bowl of cool water, swirling them around to remove any dirt and then quickly rinsing them with cool running water. If the leaves are really big, tear them up first. Be careful about using aluminium pans as the oxalates contained in the chard will react with the metal and cause the pot to discolour.

Since chard stalks are thicker in texture, they will take longer to cook than the leaves, so their cooking should be started a few minutes earlier. Large chard leaves are best for quick boiling rather than steaming since this helps to free the oxalic acids and makes the chard less bitter. Here are some suggestions for adding spinach into other dishes:
- Swiss chard leaves can be used like cabbage leaves to wrap around vegetable and grains into a neat little package. Bake in a medium-heat oven.
- Add a layer of cooked, chopped spinach to vegetable lasagne when assembling it.
- Add a layer to fish pie, between the fish and sauce and the potato topping.

STARTERS

Pork and Spinach Terrine	139
Spinach and Mushroom Salad	140
Spinach au Gratin	140
Béchamel Sauce	141
Spinach Ramekins or Timbales	141
Spinach Soup	142
Cream of Spinach Soup	143

PORK AND SPINACH TERRINE

This pâté is much more spinachy than meaty and comes from Provence in France. Serve as a light starter, which won't fill you up too much.

You will need:

    1 lb uncooked spinach beet or chard
    1 lb freshly ground fat pork
    3 teaspoons salt
    freshly ground pepper
    ¼ teaspoon mixed spice (mace, allspice, cloves)

Method
1. Wash, cook and drain the spinach. When cool, press well and chop roughly.
2. Season the meat with the salt, pepper and mixed spice.
3. Mix the meat with the spinach and turn into an oiled loaf tin or terrine. Cover with oiled paper. Stand the dish in a large pan or dish with water in.
4. Cook in an oven at 150°C (300°F, gas mark 3) for about 50 minutes.
5. Cool in the tin and turn out onto a plate. Serve with crusty bread or toast.

SPINACH AND MUSHROOM SALAD

Only use very young spinach leaves or fresh beetroot tops for this salad, otherwise the tough texture will put you off for life! You can use a ready made dressing or try one of the dressings from page 104.

You will need: **Serves 4**

    250 g (9 oz) young, fresh spinach
    250 g (9 oz) button mushrooms
    4 tablespoons salad dressing
    4 spring onions

Method

1. Wipe the mushrooms clean, cut in half and marinate them for at least an hour in the salad dressing.
2. Wash and thoroughly dry the spinach. Tear out any thick stalks and put the spinach into a salad bowl. Add the onions, mushrooms and dressing and toss to serve.

SPINACH AU GRATIN

This is another French recipe, as you may gather from the Béchamel sauce. This is really only a basic white sauce with a few added herbs and a little onion. If you prefer, just make a plain white sauce, following the instructions for the more upmarket version below.

You will need:

    450 g (1 lb) cooked spinach
    110 g (4 oz) butter
    salt and pepper
    nutmeg
    3 tablespoons grated cheese
    225 ml (8 fl oz) Béchamel sauce (see page 141)
    breadcrumbs
    110 g (4 oz) chopped lean ham

Method

1. Chop the spinach and add half of the butter. Stir over a fairly high heat until the moisture has evaporated.
2. Add the seasoning, most of the cheese and the rest of

the butter.

3. Put into a shallow dish with the ham, if used and pour over the Béchamel sauce. Top with the breadcrumbs and remaining cheese.

4. Brown in an oven or under a grill.

BÉCHAMEL SAUCE

You will need:

> 1 tablespoon flour
> 25 g (1 oz) butter or margarine
> 225 ml (8 fl oz) milk
> salt and freshly ground pepper
> ½ an onion, stuck with a whole clove
> parsley, bay leaf and thyme

Method

1. Heat the butter in a saucepan until melted and then stir in the flour. This will make a thick paste.

2. Gradually add the milk, stirring all the time. You may need to remove the pan from the heat to stop it burning. Stir until the sauce thickens evenly. If it gets lumpy, keep stirring. If all else fails, you can sieve the sauce to get rid of any lumps.

3. Add the seasoning, herbs and onion and just simmer on a very low heat for about 10–15 minutes, until the flavours are absorbed.

SPINACH RAMEKINS OR TIMBALES

Light spinach, egg and cheese starters.

You will need: Serves 4-6

> 10 g (½ oz) butter
> 450 g (1 lb) washed spinach
> 150 ml (5 oz) single cream
> 2 eggs
> salt, pepper and nutmeg
> 50 g (2 oz) grated cheese
> 25 g (1 oz) breadcrumbs

Method

1. Preheat the oven to 180°C (350°F, gas mark 4) and grease 6 ramekin dishes.
2. Melt the butter and fry the onion until soft. Add the spinach and cook for about 5 minutes then add the cream.
3. Beat the eggs in a bowl and add the spinach mixture, cheese, breadcrumbs and seasoning. Spoon into the ramekin dishes and cover with foil.
4. Place the dishes in a large dish with water in and bake for about an hour, until firm.
5. Leave to cool slightly in their dishes and turn out to serve.

SPINACH SOUP

I found this recipe in a very old book under the heading of fattening recipes. Mind you, the book also said that people suffering from diabetes should avoid cereals, including oats, pulses and most vegetables, so you can take the advice with a pinch of salt!

You will need: Serves 3-4

> 570 ml (1 pint) chicken stock
> 1 onion
> 1 potato
> 1 slice of stale bread
> 225 ml (8 fl oz) milk
> 1 teaspoon salt
> pepper
> 450 g (1 lb) spinach leaves, washed and shredded

Method

1. Place the spinach in a large saucepan with the chicken stock, bread, potato, and onion. Bring to the boil and simmer for 30 minutes.
2. Strain the liquid into a second saucepan and add the milk and seasoning. Thicken with a little cornflour if you prefer a thicker soup. Serve hot.

CREAM OF SPINACH SOUP

This is a more modern variation, with considerably more calories.

You will need:

    450 g (1 lb) washed spinach leaves
    25 g (1 oz) butter
    1 shallot or small onion, finely chopped
    1 tablespoon flour
    570 ml (1 pint) stock or water
    225 ml (8 fl oz) milk
    2 tablespoons cream or crème fraiche
    1 hard boiled egg
    lemon juice
    salt, pepper and nutmeg

Method

1. Boil the spinach in the water or stock and simmer for about 20 minutes.
2. Meanwhile, in a separate pan melt the butter and soften the onion. Stir in the flour and some of the spinach water to form a roux.
3. Strain the spinach stock into the other saucepan. Press the spinach through a sieve or blender and add to the pan. Add the milk and season well.
4. Just before serving, stir in the cream and sprinkle with nutmeg. Chop the egg roughly and add to the soup with a squeeze of lemon juice.

MAIN COURSE DISHES

Spinach Pancakes with Smoked Haddock 145

Spinach Subrics 145

Spinach Omelette 146

Spinach Soufflé 147

Spinach Soufflé with Anchovies, Ham,

Truffles or Mushrooms 147

Baked Spinach and Beetroot

Omelette/Soufflé 148

Spinach with Croutons 149

Creamed Spinach 149

Eggs Florentine 150

Pain d'Epinards 151

Spinach Tart 151

Pasta Shells Stuffed with Spinach 152

Spinach Roulade with a Cream Cheese Filling 153

Spinach Roulade with Mushroom Filling 154

Spicy Spinach with Onions 155

Spinach with Potatoes 155

SPINACH PANCAKES WITH SMOKED HADDOCK

This variation on the pancake theme can be used with a variety of fillings. You can change the fish to other white varieties or a mix of smoked and white fish.

You will need: Serves 4

50 g (2 oz) washed spinach, finely chopped
1 egg
75 g (3 oz) plain flour
salt
425 ml (15 fl oz) milk
25 g (1 oz) butter
zest of a lemon
225 g (8 oz) smoked haddock, flaked and skinned

Method
1. For the batter; sift 50 g (2 oz) of the flour and salt into a large bowl. Make a well in the centre and break in the egg. Gradually incorporate 150 ml (5 fl oz) of the milk to make a smooth batter, add the finely chopped spinach.
2. Put the butter into a saucepan and add the flour and milk to make a sauce. Stir constantly and add the lemon zest and the fish. Cook for a few more minutes.
3. Heat some butter in a frying pan and when very hot spoon in 3 tablespoons of batter. Tilt the pan to spread the mixture and cook until the pancake is firm. Turn over and brown the other side. Place on a warmed plate and repeat to make 3 more pancakes.
4. Spoon the fish and sauce onto the pancakes, roll and serve hot.

SPINACH SUBRICS

Subrics make a good accompaniment to beef or veal dishes. They are a sort of solid spinach pancake. If you prefer, use less spinach and make a thinner pancake mix which will give you more recognisable pancakes, which you could stuff with another filling, such as mushrooms.

You will need:

450 g (1 lb) cooked spinach
50 g (2 oz) butter

You will need for the pancake mix:

225 g (8 oz) plain flour
3 eggs
570 ml (1 pint) milk or water, or ½ and ½
2 tablespoons brandy
salt
2 tablespoons melted butter or oil

Method

1. First make the pancakes. Sift the flour and salt into a large bowl. Add the eggs and beat well, incorporating as much of the milk or water as is necessary to make a smooth batter. Add the brandy and leave to stand for a while.
2. Add the cooked, chopped spinach to a pan with the butter and stir until it appears to dry slightly. Add this to the batter.
3. Heat some butter or oil in a frying pan until it is very hot. Pour in a tablespoon of the spinach and batter mix and leave room to spread. Fit as many subrics in the pan as you can without them touching. Cook on each side for a minute and then turn and brown the other side.
4. Serve immediately.

SPINACH OMELETTE

You will need: Serves 2

4 eggs
250 g (9 oz) spinach, washed and finely chopped
50 g (2 oz) butter
1 tablespoon low fat plain yoghurt
salt, pepper and nutmeg

Method

1. Melt half of the butter in a pan and add the spinach, stirring over a gentle heat for 4 minutes.
2. Remove from the heat and stir in the yoghurt and seasoning.

3. Beat the eggs with pepper while you melt the rest of the butter in a clean frying pan.

4. Pour in the eggs when the butter is hot. Lift the edges to allow uncooked egg to run onto the pan base.

5. When cooked, pour over the spinach and cook for a further minute.

6. Fold in half and slide onto a warm plate to serve.

SPINACH SOUFFLÉ

This basic soufflé is a very tasty dish flavoured with spinach on its own, but can also be improved with anchovies, ham or, as a real treat, with truffles. You can use which cheese you like, although Gruyere would be a good alternative to Cheddar.

You will need:

> 3 eggs, separated
> 225 g (8 oz) cooked spinach
> 3 tablespoons grated cheese
> salt and freshly ground pepper

Method

1. Preheat the oven to 190°C (375°F, gas mark 5) and butter a soufflé dish.

2. Finely chop or puree the spinach and season well.

3. Beat the egg yolks with most of the cheese and stir in the spinach.

4. Beat the egg whites until stiff in a separate bowl.

5. Fold the egg whites into the spinach and egg yolks. Top with the left over cheese and cook for 25 minutes.

SPINACH SOUFFLÉ WITH ANCHOVIES, HAM, TRUFFLES OR MUSHROOMS

You will need:

> As above, plus either
> 1 small tin of anchovy fillets, chopped, drained and dried
> on kitchen paper
> Or 110 g (4 oz) lean ham, chopped into cubes
> Or 110 g (4 oz) thinly sliced mushrooms (or truffles)

Method

1. Follow the recipe above, adding the chopped fillets of anchovy, or ham or mushrooms with the spinach.

BAKED SPINACH AND BEETROOT OMELETTE/SOUFFLÉ

If making soufflés isn't one of your strengths, an omelette is almost as good and a lot easier. This fairly old recipe combines both the beet and the tender leaves of spinach which are then baked in the oven. In the interests of economy, flour and milk were added to make the eggs go further. Of course, you could easily leave out the flour and milk and cook the omelette in a frying pan, but I have included this recipe for interest. It could help with the cholesterol levels as well, if you are limiting your egg consumption. The pan method is better for two portions.

On a curious note, the original recipe suggested adding Brussels sprouts if you don't like beetroot, but I can't imagine that being a popular choice, what with spinach as well!

You will need: Serves 3 to 4

    110 g (4 oz) young spinach leaves
    110 g (4 oz) cooked beetroot
    1 tablespoon chopped parsley
    ½ tablespoon chopped thyme
    1 tablespoon sieved flour (optional)
    4 eggs
    50 g (2 oz) melted butter
    4 tablespoons milk (optional)
    salt and pepper

Method

1. Preheat the oven to 190°C (375°F, gas mark 5) and prepare a pie dish or pan.
2. Wash and chop the spinach with the beetroot, herbs and seasoning.
3. Beat the eggs and add the spinach and beetroot, then the flour, melted butter and milk. Mix well and put into the prepared dish.

4. Bake for 20–25 minutes.

SPINACH WITH CROUTONS

Most spinach bought nowadays is fairly clean, but it should always be washed unless the packaging states that it is already washed. Older spinach leaves will need to be stripped off the stalks. This recipe is more suited to the tougher leaves, but wherever possible, try to eat the spinach when young. If you have a steamer, that is the best way to keep the spinach from being too soggy.

You will need:

> 900 g (2 lb) spinach
> 25 g (1 oz) butter
> croutons of fried bread
> salt and pepper

Method
1. Carefully wash the leaves in plenty of water. Lift out or strain through a colander.
2. Place in a large pan. You don't need to add water. Cover and cook for a few minutes, until the spinach has wilted and reduced considerably.
3. Strain again and gently press out any excess water. You can save the water for soup or gravy stock.
4. Chop the spinach finely and stir in the butter. Season and serve with the croutons.

CREAMED SPINACH

This is a non diet version!

You will need:

> 900 g (2 lb) spinach
> 4 tablespoons cream
> 50 g (2 oz) butter
> 25 g (1 oz) flour
> salt and freshly ground pepper
> pinch of nutmeg
> Parmesan cheese for topping
> parsley (optional)

Method

1. Wash and cook the spinach as for the recipe above and then chop.
2. Melt the butter in a saucepan and stir in the flour. Put in the spinach and mix well. Add the cream and seasoning
3. Place into a heated dish and garnish with Parmesan cheese and parsley.

EGGS FLORENTINE

You will need:

> 5 eggs
> 2 lb spinach, washed
> 25 g (1 oz) butter
> grated cheese for topping

For the mornay sauce you will need:

> 25 g (1 oz) butter
> 25 g (1 oz) flour
> 8 fl oz milk
> 25 g (1 oz) Parmesan cheese
> salt and pepper
> French mustard

Method

1. Soft boil the eggs and cook the spinach in a saucepan with just the water attached to the leaves from washing.
2. Drain and chop the spinach, and press out any surplus water. Put the butter in the pan and replace the spinach. Toss to cover and heat with butter.
3. Make the sauce in the same way as for Béchamel sauce on page 141, beating in the cheese and mustard with the milk.
4. Peel the eggs and cut into halves. Arrange the spinach in a shallow dish and place the eggs on the top. Pour over the sauce and top with grated cheese.
5. Brown under a preheated grill and serve hot.

PAIN D'EPINARDS

This unusual recipe has nothing to do with bread, although the firm ring produced could be used as a bread-like crust for serving another vegetable, such as sautéed mushrooms, or even warm beetroot. If you don't have a mould, use a cake tin and place the vegetables on top to serve.

You will need:
> 900 g (2 lb) spinach
> (8 fl oz) Béchamel sauce (see page 141)
> 2 eggs
> salt, pepper and nutmeg
> 25 g (1 oz) butter

Method
1. Preheat the oven to 180°C (350°F, gas mark 4) and grease a pie dish or plain mould.
2. Wash the spinach and cook in a large saucepan with just the water attached to the leaves until tender.
3. Drain well and chop finely. Return to the pan with the butter and toss to cover.
4. Make the sauce as described, adding 2 beaten eggs at the end. Combine with the spinach and pour into the prepared mould. Cover with oiled, greaseproof paper and stand in a larger pan of water.
5. Cook for about 50 minutes, or until firm. Leave to cool for a few minutes and then turn out. Fill with mushrooms, beetroot or chosen vegetables and serve warm.

SPINACH TART

You can make this quickly and easily, especially if you use ready made pastry.

You will need:
> 110 g (4 oz) short crust pastry
> 1 medium onion or 2 shallots
> 2 eggs
> 225 g (8 oz) cooked spinach, chopped finely and well drained
> salt and freshly ground pepper

large pinch grated nutmeg
175 g (6 oz) Gruyere cheese, sliced thinly
110 ml (4 fl oz) single cream

Method
1. Preheat the oven to 180°C (350°F, gas mark 4) and grease a flan dish or tin.
2. Roll out the pastry to line the flan dish.
3. Melt the butter in a pan and gently cook the onion.
4. Beat the eggs with the cream and stir in the onion and spinach. Season with the salt, pepper and nutmeg.
5. Put half of the cheese on top of the pastry and then pour in the spinach mixture. Finish with the rest of the cheese.
6. Bake for about 30 minutes, until golden. Serve hot or cold.

PASTA SHELLS STUFFED WITH SPINACH

The trick here is to use really big pasta shells. If you can't find them you could still make the filling and serve on a bed of small pasta shapes.

You will need: Serves 4
20 large pasta shells
900 g (2 lb) washed spinach
3 garlic cloves, crushed
175 g (6 oz) low fat soft cheese
300 g (11 oz) low fat yoghurt
2 tablespoons tomato puree
salt, pepper and nutmeg
zest and juice of a lemon

Method
1. Cook the pasta shells in plenty of boiling water until tender (about 8 minutes) and then drain immediately.
2. Chop the spinach and place in a large pan with just the water attached to the leaves. Cook for about 4–5 minutes, until wilted. Don't overcook. Drain and press to remove excess water.
3. Mix the spinach with the cheese and garlic and season well. Leave to cool.

4. Mix the yoghurt with the tomato puree, zest and lemon juice. Season with pepper.

5. Stuff the shells with the cooled spinach mix and arrange on plates, pouring the sauce over to finish. Serve chilled.

SPINACH ROULADE
WITH A CREAM CHEESE FILLING

This savoury roll dish is really impressive to serve up, especially if you manage to keep it in one piece. The answer is to make sure the tin is fully greased and lined and that you don't have to answer the phone at the crucial moment of rolling. It's still worth a try. An extra pair of hands helps, but I have been known to cheat and secure it with a few cocktail sticks if it is too springy. Just warn people that the sticks are in there somewhere!

You will need: **Serves 4**

> 450 g (1 lb) washed spinach
> 4 eggs, separated
> salt, pepper and nutmeg

For the filling you will need:

> 110 g (4 oz) low fat fromage frais
> 1 onion
> 50 g (2 oz) grated Cheddar cheese
> 2 tablespoons low fat crème fraiche
> 10 g (½ oz) butter

Method

1. Grease and line a Swiss roll tin with baking parchment.

2. Place the spinach in a large pan with just the water attached to the leaves and cook for about 5 minutes, until just wilted. Drain, press out excess water and chop finely.

3. Preheat the oven to 200°C (400°F, gas mark 6).

4. Beat the egg yolks with the nutmeg, salt and pepper. Add the spinach when cooled slightly.

5. In a separate bowl, whisk the egg whites until frothy and stiff and fold into the spinach until well mixed.

6. Spread onto the baking sheet and cook for 15-20

minutes, until firm to the touch.

7. Meanwhile melt the butter and fry the onion for about 5 minutes. Remove from the heat and mix with the fromage frais and crème fraiche. Season well.

8. When the roll is cooked, turn it out onto a clean piece of baking parchment. Carefully peel off the old piece of parchment and spread over the cheese filling quickly. Then using the clean paper to help you, roll the whole thing up like a Swiss roll, lengthways. Cut into slices and serve hot.

SPINACH ROULADE WITH MUSHROOM FILLING

I much prefer this alternative filling, especially good if you have to limit the amount of cheese and fat you consume.

You will need:

    450 g (1 lb) washed spinach
    4 eggs, separated
    salt, pepper and nutmeg

You will need for the mushroom filling:

    175 g (6 oz) mushrooms
    150 ml (5 fl oz) skimmed milk
    1 tablespoon flour
    2 tablespoons olive oil
    1 onion, chopped
    pepper

Method

1. Follow steps 1 to 6 for the spinach roulade with cream cheese.

2. While the pancake is cooking, heat the oil in a pan and fry the onion until soft. Add the mushrooms and stir fry for 2—3 minutes.

3. Stir in the flour and the milk and season well, simmering for another 2 minutes.

4. Complete step 8 as above.

SPICY SPINACH WITH ONIONS

I love using spices in cooking. This dish is equally good with other spicy dishes or with roast chicken and an ideal way of using up a glut of perpetual spinach.

You will need: **Serves 4**

900 g (2 lb) spinach, washed and cut into strips
110 g (4 oz) onions, finely chopped
1 teaspoon fresh ginger, grated or finely chopped
½ hot green chilli (optional)
4 tablespoons oil
½ teaspoon salt
pinch of sugar
125 ml water

Method

1. Heat the oil in a large pan and stir in the onions. Add the spinach, ginger, salt, sugar and chilli. Stir and cook for about 5 minutes.
2. Add the water to the pan and cover tightly. Continue to cook over a very low heat for another 5 minutes.
3. Remove the lid and boil away any excess liquid before serving.

SPINACH WITH POTATOES (SAAG ALOO)

This is an easy dish to make and can be very filling, ideal for a cold winter's night. Serve with other Indian dishes or roast lamb.

You will need: **Serves 4**

350 g (12 oz) potatoes, peeled and cubed
350 g (12 oz) fresh spinach leaves, washed and chopped
110 g (4 oz) onions, chopped
2 cloves garlic, crushed
2 tablespoons oil
1 teaspoon ground cumin seeds
1 teaspoon ground coriander seeds
1 teaspoon whole black mustard seeds
pinch cayenne pepper
salt
150 ml (5 fl oz) water

Method

1. Heat the oil in a thick bottomed pan. Add the black mustard seeds and cook until they start to pop. Add the onions and garlic and fry for 2—3 minutes.

2. Add the potatoes, cayenne and other spices. Stir and fry to combine. Add the spinach, salt and 2 tablespoons of water. Bring to the boil and then add the rest of the water. Cover and lower the heat.

3. Cook until the potatoes are tender — about 20 minutes. Check that the liquid has not all been absorbed and adjust if necessary.

OTHER RECIPES WITH SPINACH

SPINACH PESTO

You can use this as a pasta sauce, or add quantities to sauces and stews. It will keep in the fridge for up to 3 days.

You will need:

1 knob butter
2 tablespoons olive oil
2 cloves garlic, crushed
450 g (1 lb) spinach or chard
50 g (2 oz) toasted pine nuts
110 g (4 oz) fresh Parmesan or pecorino cheese, grated
fresh coriander leaves

Method

1. Wash the spinach thoroughly and drain well.

2. Melt the butter in a saucepan with the olive oil. Stir in the spinach and cook for 5 minutes, then turn off the heat. Chop the leaves well in the pan.

3. Add the coriander leaves, pine nuts and Parmesan.

4. Puree the mixture until it looks like pesto.

SPINACH WINE

Spinach is low in acid so needs lemons to provide the right proportion. As for beetroot wine, the yeast needs to be prepared before adding to the liquid. If you use fresh yeast for the fermentation, prepare it with a little lukewarm water before you start. If dried yeast is used, follow the instructions provided on the packet.

You will need:

2½ lb spinach
1 gallon water
2 lemons
3 lb sugar
1 lb raisins, washed, stoned and chopped
¾ oz fresh yeast or 1 level teaspoon dried yeast

Method

1. Wash the spinach carefully to remove any dirt. Boil for 30 minutes in the water, and then strain off the liquid.
2. Meanwhile, remove the zest from the lemons and the juice. Put these into a large bowl with the raisins and sugar and pour over the liquid spinach water, stirring well to dissolve the sugar.
3. When cooled, add the prepared yeast. Pour into a jar with a fermentation lock and leave to ferment until all bubbles have stopped forming.
4. Siphon off into a clean jar and cork firmly. Leave for about 6 months and then bottle.
5. Keep for a year before drinking.

Alphabetical List of Spinach Beets and Chards

A

Action
Albina Vereduna
Alvro Mono
Avenger
Avon

B

Big Red
Big Top
Bikores
Blankoma White
Blood Red
Bluto
Bolivar
Boltardy
Bonel
Boro
Bright Yellow
Bright Lights
Bull's Blood
Burgundy
Burpees Golden
Burpee Redhart
Burpee White
Butter Slicer

C

Cardenal
Carillon
Centurion
Chariot
Charlotte
Cheltenham Green Top
Chicago Red
Chilean

Chioggia
Citation
Cook's Delight
Covent Garden
Crapaudine
Crosby Green Top
Crosby's Egyptian
Cylindra,
Cyndor

D

Darko
Derwent Globe
Detroit
Detroit Bolivar
Detroit Crimson Globe
Detroit Dark Red
Detroit Little Ball
Detroit Lora
Detroit Supreme
Detroit Tardel
Detroit Rubidus
Dobbie's Purple
Dorée
Dwergina

E

Early Bassano
Early Blood
Early Bunch
Early Warrior
Early Wonder
Early Wonder Staysgreen
Eastern Wonder
Egyptian
Erbette

F

Fordhook Giant
Formanova
Forono
Feuer Kugel

G

Garnet
Gladiator
Green Top Bunching

K

King Red
Kugel

L

Large White
Libero
Long Blood Red
Lucullus
Lutz Green Leaf

M

MacGregor's Favourite
Mammoth Long
Modella
Modena
Monaco
Moneta
Mono King Burgundy
Monogram
Monopoly
Moulin Rouge

N

Nobol

P

Pablo
Perpetual (Spinach beet)
Preco
Pronto

R

Rainbow Chard
Red Ace
Red Arrow
Red Ball
Red Dart
Red Midrib
Red Russian
Red Velvet
Redpack
Regala
Rhubarb Chard
Rocket
Rosette
Royal Delight
Royal Red
Ruby Chard
Ruby Queen

S

Sangria
Seneca
Smooth Crosby
Snow white
Soloist
Sweetheart
Swiss Chard

T

Tall Top

U

Ukrainian

V

Vulcan

W

Winter King

Y

Yellow Intermediate
Mangel

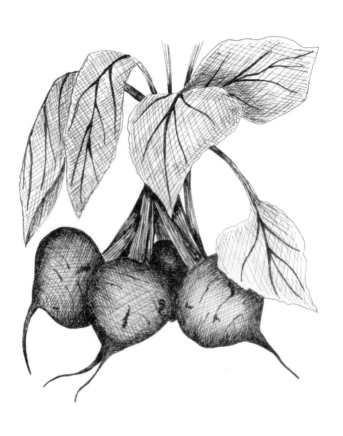